EMPIRE

FILM QUIZ BOOK

EMPIRE
FILM QUIZ BOOK

Written and Researched by
IAN FREER

Picture Research by
DEBORAH BROWN

ANDRE
DEUTSCH

First published in 1997 by
André Deutsch Ltd
106 Great Russell Street
London
WC1B 3LJ
www.vci.co.uk

André Deutsch is a subsidiary of VCI plc

A catalogue record for this book is available from the British Library.

ISBN 0 233 99234 0

Designed by Bradley Davis
Printed and bound Butler & Tanner, Frome, Somerset

Contents

Introduction

by IAN NATHAN, Editor, Empire

If there is one thing Empire magazine stands for it is the enjoyment of movies. Of course we appreciate a spot of intelligent, even intellectual, film discussion (usually down the pub, over an unpolished table of ever growing empties) but how can you start wittering on about comparable semiotic referencing if the hairs on the back of your neck don't start tingling when the lights lower and a hush descends on the expectant audience? From Star Wars to Einstein, from Tarantino to Top Gun, film should, above all, excite. And Empire gets excited about films.

And with such enthusiasm we have turned our powers to the ultimate test of filmgoing knowledge. What you hold in your hands is not some yawnsome academic examination or anally retentive nerd assessor but a bona fide test of how well you know and enjoy film. There are genre questions on such favourites as Sci-fi, James Bond, Westerns and Horror (do you know how many escaped in The Great Escape or which Western features Marlon Brando in drag?). There's Hollywood – from the Oscars to the directors to the lovers (who was Tom Cruise married to before Nicole Kidman?). We've also picked nine movies and one collective you ought to have sussed if you want to have an iota of filmic credibility (just how well do you really know Blade Runner or The Blues Brothers?). After a splendid picture round, for a bit of visual stimuli, we focus on elements that are quintessentially Empire. Looking at film from a more oblique angle there are posers on taglines, opening lines, character names and on some of Empire's official cinematic 'Shite'. And just in case anyone starts to get cocky, the Bloody Hard Section poses the ultimate challenge – OK then, who invented popcorn? Finally, to stir up some communal spirit we round off with some team games that will keep your dinner parties alive for years to come.

Written, researched and edited in the inimitable Empire style, you'll find this book totally unlike every other stuffy movie quiz tome of the past. Just as Empire is unlike any other movie magazine you care to mention. It's not going to be easy, but, hey, if you get stuck you can always go back and watch the movies in question.

Enjoy!

Ian Nathan
Editor

Genres

In the heyday of Hollywood, genre movies ruled the roost. The expectations set up by reusable storylines, stars, settings and set pieces meant everybody knew where they stood; a teary goodbye at a train station could only be a romance. Audiences liked the comfort and convenience offered by such easily recognizable forms. But as film history evolved, the slow-joes in the back rows grew more sophisticated, forcing film makers to bend the rules and play with the conventions to keep their movies fresh. Most often, this meant injecting a reality check – compare the simplistic shoot-'em-up Westerns of the thirties with the brooding complexity of a Clint Eastwood effort. It could also mean exploding genres by combining them – Star Wars liberally dips into science fiction, swashbucklers, Westerns and war movies – or cleverly playing on our knowledge of film history à la Tarantino. This opening section, therefore, tackles the multiplicity of genres, both in their traditional and modern incarnations...

'I'm not bad. I'm just drawn that way…' *

Animation

Welcome to the eye popping, anvil dropping world of animation. The process of photographing still pictures and objects to create movement has come a long way since the first cartoon Gertie The Dinosaur predated Jurassic Park by some 84 years: from the scathing satire of The Simpsons, the sublime CG imagery of Toy Story and Disney's single-handed revitalisation of the musical, the cartoon has grown up. And then some. To wit: you may know all the words to The Flintstones theme tune but do you really know your ACME from your elbow?

1) Name the villainess of 101 Dalmatians.

2) What is the name of the action fuelled animation style made popular in Japan?

3) Name the sequel to the 1977 Disney hit The Rescuers.

4) Name the director of Toy Story.

5) In which film do Tom and Jerry hoof with Gene Kelly?

6) Who provided the voices for the following:
   (a) Bugs Bunny
   (b) Shere Khan in The Jungle Book
   (c) Jessica Rabbit in Who Framed Roger Rabbit
   (d) Genie in Aladdin
   (e) Esmerelda in The Hunchback Of Notre Dame

7) In which movie would you find Thumper?

8) Name the Bristol-based animation company behind Wallace and Gromit.

9) Michael Jordan is one human star of Space Jam. Name the other.

10) Which legendary animator links Jason And The Argonauts and The Seventh Voyage Of Sinbad?

11) Hanna–Barbera are legends within the animation field. Christian names please.

12) Which visionary Hollywood director was behind The Nightmare Before Christmas?

13) In which 1960s music orientated cartoon was the Kingdom of Pepperland attacked by the Blue Meanies?

14) Name the big screen adaptation of The Magic Roundabout.

15) Who directed Fritz The Cat?

16) In which films do the following songs appear:
   (a) The Bare Necessities
   (b) When You Wish Upon A Star
   (c) Zip-A-Dee-Do-Dah
   (d) Be Our Guest
   (e) You've Got A Friend

17) Who links The Lion King with Star Wars?

18) An oldie but still a goldie: name the seven dwarfs.

19) In which film did Mickey Mouse become the Sorcerer's Apprentice?

20) At the end of Warner Bros cartoons, which character says Th-Th-Th That's All Folks?

*Jessica Rabbit in Who Framed Roger Rabbit? (1988)

'That's no moon. It's a space station…'*

Science Fiction

Paper plates doubling as flying saucers, the hokiest dialogue imaginable ('Take me to your leader!') and performances carved out of balsawood. From such inauspicious beginnings, science fiction has flourished into big budget bonanzas. Wowing us with fantastical visions whilst fuelling questions about the future, the possibility of alien life and why all Star Wars stormtroopers are such rubbish shots. To further add to these complexities, undertake this galactic grilling for a maximum interplanetary-intellect interface. And remember, in space no one can hear your brain tick over…

1) Name the spaceship in Alien.

2) Who played The Man Who Fell To Earth?

3) Which landmark science fiction movie features Leonard Rossiter?

4) Where do the travellers journey to in Fantastic Voyage?

5) What was Carlo Rambaldi's contribution to E.T.: The Extra Terrestrial?

6) In which film did the following robots appear?
   (a) Robby The Robot
   (b) Gort
   (c) Huey and Dewey
   (d) VINCENT and Old Bob
   (e) Number 5

7) What hymn did Scotty play on the bagpipes over Spock's funeral at the end of Star Trek 2: The Wrath Of Khan?

8) What is the name of the alien played by Natasha Henstridge in Species?

9) Which SF comedy features the orgasmatron?

10) 'Keep Watching The Skies' is the ominous warning at the end of which S/F classic?

11) The War Of The Worlds is based on the novel by which celebrated SF author?

12) Complete the following lyric: 'Flash...'

13) Which film features the characters Captain Dildano and Durand-Durand?

14) Which future superstar made his feature film debut in The Blob?

15) Which special effects technique was used to create the shape shifting transformations of the T-1000 in Terminator 2: Judgment Day?

16) Which actor in what film wants to 'whop E.T.'s ass'?

17) Who directed the following SF movies?
   (a) Metropolis
   (b) Zardoz
   (c) Dune
   (d) Predator
   (e) Men In Black

18) Doolittle, Boiler, Pinback, Talby and Powell are the motley crew of which spaceship?

19) Who played the title role in Starman?

20) A Close Encounter of The Third Kind is scientific speak for contact with an alien species. What are close encounters of the first and second kind?

*Obi Wan Kenobi (Alec Guinness) in Star Wars (1977)

'Pay attention 007…'*

James Bond

His name is Bond. James Bond – licensed to kill, deploy cool gadgetry and raise his eyebrows in a smarmy manner. Making his first big screen appearance in 1962, the cinematic exploits of the British Secret Service Agent have raked in over one billion dollars worldwide and display as much 'formula' as any fully-fledged genre. The action inevitably takes in larger-than-life plots, exotic locales, gorgeous girls ('Oh, Jemsh'), villains with silly names, death defying stunts and a double entendre to finish ('Just keeping the British end up, sir!'). In honour of Blighty's finest, try the following Bond bafflers – for your eyes only, naturally…

1) Name the creator of James Bond.

2) Name the six actors who have portrayed James Bond and their 007 debut movies.

3) Why was the book Licence Revoked retitled Licence To Kill by the time it reached the big screen?

4) Who is Bond's CIA cohort?

5) Match the Bond babe to the actress:
   1) Dr Holly Goodhead   (a) Honor Blackman
   2) Honey Ryder   (b) Britt Ekland
   3) Solitaire   (c) Lois Chiles
   4) Pussy Galore   (d) Jane Seymour
   5) Mary Goodnight   (e) Ursula Andress

6) What does S.P.E.C.T.R.E. stand for?

7) Name the only theme tune singer to appear in a title sequence.

8) Who played the metal tooth henchman Jaws and in which films?

9) Name the unusual anatomical feature belonging to the character played by Christopher Lee in The Man With The Golden Gun.

10) Name the two hitmen dispatched to kill Bond in Diamonds Are Forever.

11) Which Bond girl was also a Charlie's Angel?

12) Which geological feature provided the hideout for Blofeld in You Only Live Twice?

13) Name the producer most readily associated with bringing Bond to the big screen.

14) Finish this classic 007 dialogue exchange: 'Do you expect me to talk, Goldfinger…?'

15) Name the title song not to feature the name of the film in the lyric.

16) Which Bond film features Rowan Atkinson?

17) Name three actors who have portrayed the cat-stroking Blofeld.

18) In which British studio would you find the 007 stage?

19) In which films do the following vehicles appear?
    (a) A submersible Lotus Esprit
    (b) Little Nelly
    (c) A dry land gondola
    (d) A stolen Moonbuggy
    (e) An ejector seated Aston Martin

20) Who played the short, bespectacled villain whose motive was to kill all men taller than himself and in which film?

*Line delivered by Q (Desmond Llewellyn) every time he gives Bond a run down of the gadgetry

'Do you want to see something really scary…?' *

Horror

A suave Transylvanian count sinks his fangs into helpless virgins; a possessed girl vomits pea soup; dumb Yank teenagers explore dark cellars knowing there is a crazed maniac on the loose. If any genre has remained consistently popular over the course of Hollywood history, it is the horror flick – the jolts and joys of being scared stiff in the comfort and safety of a packed auditorium never seem to diminish. Prepare to search the darkest corners of your movie memories to answer posers on those scare-fests best watched through the cracks in the fingers…

1) Where do the wispy spectres in Poltergeist emanate from?

2) Name the pub visited by the yank hitchhikers in An American Werewolf in London.

3) Give the three rules you should follow when keeping a Gremlin.

4) Which Italian maestro directed Suspiria and Inferno?

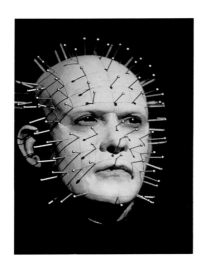

5) Which films featured the following horror icons?
    (a) Pinhead
    (b) Jason Voorhees
    (c) Leatherface
    (d) Michael Myers

6) Who played the newlyweds in Rosemary's Baby?

7) Name the book at the centre of the Evil Dead saga.

8) Which studio was synonymous with British Horror in the 60s and 70s?

9) What was Damien's surname in The Omen trilogy?

10) Who plays Freddie Krueger in The Nightmare On Elm Street series?

11) In which David Cronenberg films do the following characters appear; Darryl Revok, Max Renn, Seth Brundle?

12) Who wrote the book on which The Exorcist is based?

13) Name the hotel in The Shining.

14) What is unusual about the cast of John Carpenter's 1982 remake of The Thing?

15) Who played the title role in The Bride Of Frankenstein?

16) Who directed the 1932 classic Freaks?

17) Which current Hollywood hotshots made early appearances in the following low budget fright-fests?
    (a) He Knows You're Alone
    (b) The Burning
    (c) Return To The Texas Chainsaw Massacre
    (d) Critters 3

18) Which modern horror classic famously held joint casting sessions with Star Wars?

19) What is Courteney Cox's profession in Scream?

20) Which comedy horror is set in the Bide-A-Wee Rest Home, Hocombe Woods?

*Dan Aykroyd in Twilight Zone: The Movie (1983)

'A man's gotta do what a man's gotta do' *

Westerns

Known in the early days of movies as 'horse operas' or 'oaters', the Western always promises a multitude of pleasures; the rugged grandeur of wide open spaces; a tense showdown in a deserted street, topped off by the pre-requisite tumbleweed; a runaway stagecoach besieged by marauding injuns. Besides, it's the only place characters can use the words 'Varmint' and 'Pardner' without suffering howls of derision. Amazingly, the most distinctive of American genres has also been relocated to the most unlikely milieus – witness Italian 'Spaghetti' flicks and even the UK's own Carry On Cowboy recreated the Wild West in sunny Surrey. So saddle up and ride off into the sunset to face this posse of sharp shooting teasers. Are the questions easy? The hell they are…

1) Who directed Once Upon A Time In The West?

2) Who respectively played Butch Cassidy and The Sundance Kid? For extra brownie points, who played the same characters in the 1978 prequel?

3) In the 1980 mega flop Western, what *is* Heaven's Gate?

4) Which Buddy Holly song earned its title from a line of dialogue from which classic Western?

5) Which 1985 Western features John Cleese?

6) What is the name of Gene Wilder's character in Blazing Saddles?

7) In which Western, and playing which character, did John Wayne earn his only Oscar?

8) Name the theme song to High Noon.

9) Which Western features Marlon Brando in drag?

10) In Dances With Wolves, which actress was the object of Kevin Costner's affection and what was the name of her character?

11) Which Western stars Jodie Foster?

12) Name the animated character who 'goes west' in the sequel to An American Tale.

13) Victor Mature, Kirk Douglas, Val Kilmer and Dennis Quaid have all portrayed which legendary Western figure?

14) Which Western opens with the sight of small children torturing insects?

15) Name the location that often forms the backdrop for John Ford's classic Westerns.

16) Name Clint Eastwood's character in Unforgiven.

17) Which actresses played the titular foursome in Bad Girls?

18) Name the Western that proved to be John Candy's last film.

19) What is the name of the calf delivered by Billy Crystal in City Slickers?

20) 'Hey, Blondie...' Name the film.

*Alan Ladd in Shane (1953) although everybody thinks John Wayne said it

'If it bends, it's funny' *

Comedy

From the intellectual subtlety of Woody Allen to the puerile face-pulling of Jim Carrey, from Chaplin's bowler hat to Sid James' cardigan, cinema has continually satisfied the most natural in-born desire known to humankind – the need to laugh. Comedy in moviedom comes in various guises – slapstick, satire, spoof and, if you're French, Jerry Lewis. If it is done well, the end result is always the same: uncontrollable side-splittage. If you can keep a straight face, test your knowledge on those magic movies that have instant access to the bone marked 'funny'...

1) What is the name of the army regiment who wear nothing under their kilts in Carry On Up The Khyber?

2) Where did Jim Carrey and Jeff Daniels travel to in Dumb And Dumber?

3) In which comedies would you find the following characters?
          a) Duckface
          b) Felix Unger
          c) Adrian Cronauer
          d) Nordberg
          e) Egon Spengler

4) What is the name of the geek whom Bill Murray eventually punches out in Groundhog Day?

5) Withnail And I: what is Richard E. Grant's method for convincing the police of his sobriety when tested for drunk driving?

6) This Is Spinal Tap is a parody of which 'rockumentary' by Martin Scorsese?

7) Cheech and Chong. Full names please.

8) Apart from Peter Sellers, name the other actor to portray Inspector Clouseau.

9) What is the name of the Dolphin tracked down by pet 'tec Ace Ventura?

10) 'Assume the position!' Name the film.

11) In Gregory's Girl, what did Gregory's father do for a living?

12) Name the French director of M. Hulot's Holiday and Playtime who was renowned for his visual comedy.

13) Which event do Jack Lemmon and Tony Curtis witness that forces them to don drag during Some Like It Hot?

14) Name the eponymous unfortunate who thinks his employment chances have improved when he is offered a 'blowjob'.

15) Who directed The Ladykillers?

16) In which film does Charlie Chaplin turn two skewered bread rolls into feet and stage a mini dance spectacular?

17) Match the Woody Allen dialogue to the correct film.
   1) 'Hey don't knock masturbation. It's sex with someone I love.'
   2) 'I have a gub'
   3) 'Where did you study medicine? Transylvania?'
   4) 'The last time I was inside a woman was when I visted the Statue of Liberty'
   5) 'Nobody moves or the nose gets it!'
(a) Sleeper (b) Crimes And Misdemeanours (c) Annie Hall (d) Stardust Memories
(e) Take The Money And Run

18) Who wrote the paperbacks on which Robin Asquith's Confessions (Of A Window Cleaner, Pop Performer etc) films are based?

19) What is Groucho Marx's real name?

20) Life Of Brian: name the two Romans who produce sniggers amongst centurions when their names are mentioned by the lisping Michael Palin?

*The comic philosophy of Lester (Alan Alda) in Crimes And Misdemeanours (1989)

'Gotta sing! gotta dance!…' *

Musicals

'Hey kids! We can do the show right here in the barn!' Often with more corn than Kansas, the musical overflowed with sentiment, vitality and toe tappin' tunes that made sitting still in the seat absolutely impossible. In these cynical times, however, musicals are a bit thin on the ground; the notion of people just bursting into song to express their feelings may be a bit tough to swallow. Still, with the likes of Evita keeping the flame alive, nothing sums up the glitz of Hollywood or the power of movies better than an all-singing, all-dancing extravaganza – so dig out those dancing shoes, grab a partner and waltz your way through the following quick-step questions…

1) Who sang the theme tune for Fame?

2) Fred Astaire and Ginger Rogers. Real names please.

3) Which 80s musical features a song and dance routine by Christopher Walken?

4) High Society is a musical remake of which 40s comedy?

5) Don Lockwood, Cathy Selden and Cosmo Brown. Who played these characters and in which classic musical?

6) Who directed Tommy?

7) 'A kiss on the hand may be quite continental…' Name this song from Gentlemen Prefer Blondes and state the way in which it relates to Madonna.

8) Name the rival gangs in West Side Story.

9) What were the respective wishes of The Scarecrow, The Tin Man and The Lion in The Wizard Of Oz?

10) Which musical pairs Rick Moranis and Steve Martin?

11) Who directed Cabaret and All That Jazz?

12) Name the character played by Marlon Brando in Guys And Dolls.

13) Which 1994 film started life as a musical, then had all but one of its songs removed before release?

14) Which musical features The Trolley Song?

15) Name the type of weaponry favoured by gangsters in Bugsy Malone.

16) According to Julie Andrews in The Sound Of Music, what is (a) Do (b) Re (c) Mi?

17) Which legendary choreographer/director behind Gold Diggers Of 1935 and Babes In Arms was famed for his bird's-eye-view camera shot?

18) Match the song to the film.
   1) You'll Never Walk Alone
   2) Who Will Buy This Wonderful Morning
   3) Some Enchanted Evening
   4) I Was Born Under A Wanderin' Star
   5) Oh What A Beautiful Morning
(a) Paint Your Wagon (b) Oklahoma (c) Carousel (d) South Pacific (e) Oliver!

19) In which musical would you find the character Truly Scrumptious?

20) Name the three actors who portayed aliens in Julien Temple's science fiction musical Earth Girls Are Easy.

*Line belted out by Gene Kelly in Singin' In The Rain (1952)

23

'I feel it in my fingers, I feel it in my toes' *

Chick Flicks

Boy meets girl. Boy gets girl. Boy loses girl. Boy gets girl again. Older than what experts are prone to call 'the hills', this simplistic storyline has produced more handkerchief usage than a flu epidemic. A good romantic movie – or, in modern parlance, 'the date movie' or 'chick flick' – not only wears its heart on its sleeve but also on every other piece of its apparel, leaving no heartstring untugged before coming up trumps with an indefatigably feel-good finale. So wipe those tears away and lend a compassionate ear to these posers concerning love and loss, movie style. If you can't answer them, don't worry – there are plenty more fish in the sea…

1) William Shakespeare's Romeo And Juliet (1997): who plays the starcross'd lovers?

2) Name Audrey Hepburn's character in Breakfast At Tiffany's.

3) Name the first Hollywood movie to feature a French kiss.

4) Which single word answer does Patrick Swayze use to return his affection for Demi Moore in Ghost?

5) Name the two actors who battle over Holly Hunter in The Piano.

6) Name the film that all the women blub over in Sleepless In Seattle. For a bonus point, what film does Tom Hanks jokily suggest reduces him to tears?

7) 'Oh Jerry, don't let's ask for the moon. We have the stars.' Name this classic weepie.

8) Name the Academy Award winning song from Dirty Dancing. And the two vocalists who sang it.

9) Who played Tom Cruise's love interest in the following:
    (a) Top Gun
    (b) Cocktail
    (c) Jerry Maguire
    (d) The Color Of Money?

10) Roy Harold Scherer and Doris von Kappelhoff are the real names of which legendary on-screen romantic couple?

11) What musical instrument does Alan Rickman play in Truly, Madly, Deeply?

12) Who plays the snooty shop manager in Pretty Woman?

13) How many times does Bogie say 'Here's looking at you, kid' in Casablanca?

14) Who wrote the novel upon which Love Story is based?

15) Who played the young lovers in Before Sunrise?

16) Name the legendary producer of Gone With The Wind.

17) According to Janeane Garofalo in The Truth About Cats And Dogs, what do men do when Uma Thurman 'pukes'?

18) Who played Zack Mayo and Paula in which classic 80s blub-fest?

19) What is the name of Daryl Hannah's mermaid in Splash?

20) What is the classic response given by the elderly diner in the deli to Meg Ryan's faked orgasm in When Harry Met Sally?

*Opening line to the Wet Wet Wet recorded ballad for Four Weddings And A Funeral (1994)

'Prepare to go ballistic' *

Blockbusters

At one end of the moviemaking scheme of things are 'quiet' little films which the critics love, which win bucketloads of awards and nobody goes to see. At the other end are the blockbusters; the tub thumping, rollercoasting, crowd pleasing epics. Filled to the brim with fist fights, spectacle and things blowing up in gut tightening slow motion, in short, they are exactly the kind of experiences cinema was invented for. Buckle up, don that charred white vest and prepare to pit your wits against the behemoths that dominate summer movie going – the busters of block…

1) Who plays Jack Traven and Annie Porter in which high octane hit?

2) How many POWs escape in The Great Escape?

3) Name the producer-director team behind Independence Day.

4) Put these classic Arnie kiss-off lines into their correct films:
    1) 'Consider that a divorce!'
    2) 'Hasta la vista, baby!'
    3) 'Stick around!'
    4) 'He was a pain in the neck!'
    5) 'To be or not to be. *Not* to be!'
(a) Terminator 2: Judgement Day (b) The Last Action Hero (c) The Running Man
(d) Total Recall (e) Predator

5) In Back To The Future, what speed does the De Lorean have to reach to make time travel possible?

6) What was the tagline for the first Superman poster?

7) Who sang the theme tune to Ghostbusters?

8) What links Lethal Weapon to Predator?

9) 'Never rub another man's rhubarb!' Which actor delivered this line and in which film?

10) In Raiders Of The Lost Ark, how did the Nazis obtain the pattern for the headpiece to the Staff Of Ra?

11) Name the three movies featuring CIA Agent Jack Ryan and the two actors who have portrayed him. For extra kudos, who wrote the novels upon which the films are based?

12) Why is the tornado sensor in Twister nicknamed 'Dorothy'?

13) Who plays the villain in Cliffhanger?

14) What is Rambo's Christian name?

15) Who directed The Guns Of Navarone?

16) In Under Siege, Steven Seagal is a Navy SEAL masquerading as what?

17) Who played the Harrison Ford role in The Fugitive on the long running TV series?

18) Can you answer the following Die Hard–related posers?
    (a) What is the name of the building under siege?
    (b) What is the name of Alan Rickman's character?
    (c) Who plays Bruce Willis' wife?
    (d) What cowboy code name does Willis give to the cop on the ground?
    (e) How does Bruce Willis hide his gun in the final showdown with Rickman?

19) Where does the heartstopping finale of Mission: Impossible take place?

20) Name four dinosaur species which feature prominently in Jurassic Park.

*Tagline for the John Travolta/Christian Slater vehicle, Broken Arrow (1996)

'Ever since I can remember, I wanted to be a gangster' *

Crime

From the rat-a-tat machine guns and concrete overcoats of the gangsters of yore to the cool shades and botched heists of the modern day thief, the movies are often at their best when exploring the twilight worlds and attractive amorality which operates on the other side of the law. Crime very rarely pays for the characters but for us, in the audience, the genre remains endlessly rewarding…

1) What is the name of the character played by Al Pacino in Scarface?

2) In which snowbound town is the action of Fargo set?

3) Which classic caper concludes with the song 'The Self Preservation Society'?

4) Match the Reservoir Dog to his right colour;
    (1) Mr Blonde   (a) Quentin Tarantino
    (2) Mr Pink   (b) Harvey Keitel
    (3) Mr White   (c) Michael Madsen
    (4) Mr Brown   (d) Tim Roth
    (5) Mr Orange   (e) Steve Buscemi

5) Can you name the other film that boasts colour-coded criminals as characters?

6) Walter Neff and Phyllis Dietrichsen are the partners in crime in which classic *film noir*?

7) Finish this classic dialogue from The Untouchables: 'He pulls a knife. You pull a gun…'

8) What is unusual about the twenty-five minute heist sequence in Rififi?

9) Name the novelists behind Bogie classics The Big Sleep and The Maltese Falcon.

10) Who played Harold Shand and in what film?

11) What car did Steve McQueen drive in Bullitt?

12) L.A. Takedown was an early version of which 1996 crime thriller?

13) Which part of Jack Nicholson's anatomy gets cut with a knife in Chinatown and who plays the perpetrator of the slicing?

14) Who composed the haunting theme to Get Carter?

15) In The Big Heat, what does Glenn Ford throw in Gloria Grahame's face during a fit of rage?

16) Who directed The Usual Suspects?

17) Name the murder weapon in Basic Instinct.

18) Do you know the following about GoodFellas?
   (a) What is the name of Robert De Niro's character?
   (b) What song is playing when Henry and Karen walk through the Copa club?
   (c) Name the editor of GoodFellas.
   (d) What film did GoodFellas lose out to for the Best Picture Oscar?
   (e) What links GoodFellas to Woody Allen's Mighty Aphrodite?

19) What phrase in Donnie Brasco can mean anything and everything?

20) Name the couple on the run (thespians only) in the following movies:
   (a) Bonnie And Clyde
   (b) Badlands
   (c) Thieves Like Us
   (d) True Romance
   (e) Natural Born Killers

*The career ambition of Henry Hill (Ray Liotta) in GoodFellas (1990)

Hollywood

It started life as a peaceful, pastoral community until a solitary stable was converted into a studio for the purposes of making movies. By 1920 Hollywood was the world's biggest dream factory, churning out over 800 films a year, crushing hopes and making fortunes with equal rapidity and feeding the desire of a film hungry public. These days it is very much a shadow of its former self – the studio system has collapsed, the film companies have long departed, the stars even sport rips in their jeans. Even so, between the conglomerates and the call girls, the ponytails and the power breakfasts, the restaurants and the rehab, there is still an inescapable frisson of excitement, glamour, insanity and allure surrounding this modern day Never Never land. Perhaps now more than ever, Hollywood is less a geographical location and more a state of mind, a communal aspiration of luxury, power and magic that millions buy into the world over. Which is why it will probably live forever...

'The mother of all knick-knacks...' *

The Academy Awards

The Glitz! The Blubbing! The Crap Dance Routines! Established in 1928, The Academy Awards are back-slappage on an epic scale and celebrate all we love about Hollywood; fantasy, emotion, occasional controversy and highly questionable dress sense. As such, with the bimbo-esque hostess handing over the golden envelope, the nominations for the trickiest teasers about Tinseltown's biggest gong-fest are...

1) Name the only three films to win in the five major categories of Best Picture, Director, Actor, Actress and Screenplay.

2) Who won the Best Supporting Actor at the 1996 ceremony?

3) Which two actresses were involved in a tie for Best Actress in 1968?

4) Name the only sequel to win a Best Picture Oscar.

5) Name the only two women to be nominated for a Best Director Oscar.

6) Who is the only person to win an Oscar playing a member of the opposite sex?

7) Name the only person to be an Oscar winner by playing an Oscar loser.

8) Which two films share the dubious distinction of garnering 11 nominations and zilch awards?

9) Who won the Best Actor Oscar at the 1997 awards?

10) Why is Robert Opal ensconced in Oscar history?

11) Which of the following films failed to win an Oscar for Best Visual Effects?
   (a) Independence Day
   (b) Jurassic Park
   (c) Terminator 2: Judgment Day
   (d) Close Encounters Of The Third Kind

12) Name the only feature length cartoon to be nominated for a Best Picture Oscar.

13) Name the two hosts who were sandwiched between Billy Crystal's stints as Oscar MC.

14) Who did Marlon Brando send to receive his Best Actor award for The Godfather?

15) Who said the following accepting their 14" statuettes?
   (a) 'I can't deny the fact you like me! You really like me!'
   (b) 'I feel like I'm standing on magic legs!'
   (c) 'What I really want to do is act…'
   (d) 'The British Are Coming!'

16) How long does it take to make an Oscar?

17) How many Oscars did Schindler's List win?

18) Which Hollywood dynasty boasts three generations of Oscar winners?

19) Which dynamic Hollywood producer of the 30s lends his name to an honorary Oscar occasionally given out for an outstanding contribution to cinema?

20) Can you name the only Oscar ever to win an Oscar? *Clue:* it's not Schindler.

© A.M.P.A.S. ®

*Quote from Jim Carrey's memorable presentation speech for Best Cinematography in 1997

'We're just good friends…' *

Hollywood Couples

The majority of people meet their partners at work. So it is no surprise that the great and the gorgeous of Tinseltown often end up going out with their fellow stars. With a mumbled whisper of 'It'll never last', let us enter the murky world of the Hollywood dating scene – the ditching, the shacking up, the illicit affairs and the scandals in all their gory detail…

1) What was the legend adorning Johnny Depp's tattoo about Winona Ryder? For an extra point, what does it say now, after their break up?

2) Name the real life couples behind these movie characters;
   (a) Snake Plissken and Private Benjamin
   (b) Henry V and Scarlett O'Hara
   (c) Erin Grant and John McClane
   (d) Annie Reed and Gordo Cooper
   (e) Alabama Whitman and Cameron Poe

3) Who was Tom Cruise married to before Nicole Kidman?

4) Which song is allegedly about the ageing Lothario and ex-lover Warren Beatty?

5) Steven Spielberg has been married twice. To whom?

6) The number BK 4454813 06.27.95. is significant to which cinematic couple?

7) Who or what do Uma Thurman and Isabella Rossellini have in common?

8) On which movie set did Humphrey Bogart and Lauren Bacall meet?

9) 'We got married because we love each other and we decided to make a life together. We are heterosexual and monogamous and take our commitment to each other very seriously.' Which superstar duo made this statement shortly before breaking up?

10) Geena Davis and Jeff Goldblum swapped partners with which other Hollywood couple?

11) Name the film director Judy Garland married.

12) How did Daniel Day Lewis reputedly break up with Isabelle Adjani?

13) Name Jamie Lee Curtis' famous parents.

14) What is the age difference between Woody Allen and Soon Yi-Previn?

15) Julia Roberts was briefly married to which country singer?

16) Name the real life couples who share the screen in the following;
    (a) The Getaway
    (b) Bodies, Rest And Motion
    (c) Nell
    (d) Too Much
    (e) I Love You To Death

17) E.T. screenwriter Melissa Mathison has a much better-known husband. Can you name him?

18) Who has been linked to both Michelle Pfeiffer and Courteney Cox?

19) Elizabeth Taylor: what number husband was Larry Fortensky and where did the couple hold their opulent wedding ceremony?

20) Who said 'I never loved another person the way I loved myself'?

*Statement of denial by every Hollywood twosome who are secretly going out with each other

'What I really wanna do is direct...' *

Directors

They used to sport jodhpurs, berets and megaphones. Now they sport beards, baseball caps and mobile phones. They are the directors, the cine-magicians who turn words into pictures, dreams into stories and have their name bigger and brighter than anyone else, come the end credit scroll. It is an inescapable fact that if you really want to know movies, you have to be intimate with the creatives behind the camera. With the immortal cry of 'Lights! Camera! Action!', zoom in on these twenty helmer related posers to really sort out your cinematic smart-aleckness...

1) Name the director of Who Framed Roger Rabbit? and Forrest Gump.

2) Who or what links Alien and Thelma And Louise with Top Gun and Crimson Tide?

3) Quentin Tarantino was an employee of which video emporium?

4) What name are Francis Coppola, George Lucas, Steven Spielberg, Martin Scorsese and Brian De Palma collectively known as?

5) Name the Hong Kong born director of Hard Target, Broken Arrow and Face/Off.

6) Jerry Maguire director, Cameron Crowe, started his working life as a journalist for which American magazine?

7) Name the ground-breaking 80s detective series created by Heat director Michael Mann.

8) Which directors made their feature film debuts with the following?
   (a) Boyz N The Hood

(b) Speed

(c) Oh What A Lovely War!

(d) The Brothers McMullen

9) Name the character played by Ron Howard – director of Apollo 13 and Ransom – on the TV show Happy Days.

10) Who or what links action helmer Kathryn Bigelow and clothing company The Gap?

11) Which director has made films featuring Buffalo Bill, Vincent Van Gogh and Popeye as protagonists?

12) Which field of film-making would you associate with director Tex Avery?

13) What does the D.W. stand for in D.W. Griffith, the pioneering director behind Birth Of A Nation and Intolerance?

14) Which now famous director supplied the screenplays for Midnight Express, Scarface and Year Of The Dragon?

15) What does it mean when a film is 'Directed by Alan Smithee'?

16) What form does Alfred Hitchcock's obligatory cameo appearance take in North By Northwest?

17) Name the directors who turned actors for the following films;
(a) Close Encounters Of The Third Kind
(b) Scenes From A Mall
(c) Husbands And Wives
(d) Sleepless In Seattle
(e) Nightbreed

18) David Lynch originated which comic strip?

19) Brigitte Bardot and Jane Fonda were both married to which film director?

20) Name the unusual step taken by Robert Rodriguez to finance his film El Mariachi.

*Cliché spoken by every actor, actress and waiter in Hollywood with film-making aspirations

'I'll be back…' *

Sequels

In film-making lore, it is a fact universally acknowledged that if a film grosses over 80 million dollars at the U.S. box office, it will spawn a sequel. Indeed, the follow-up film is such a fixture in modern day movie schedules that scripts are being prepared and actors sign on the sequel dotted line long before the original film is released. We'll leave you to decide whether this rampant outbreak of sequelitis is just Tinseltown giving the public what they want or a sign of creative bankruptcy. For now, how up to speed (or Speed 2) are you on those films with 'Return', 'Revenge' or roman numerals in the titles?

1) Name the two cops played by Mel Gibson and Danny Glover in the Lethal Weapon series.

2) The Evening Star is the sequel to which popular blub-fest?

3) Name the film from the following sequel subtitles:
   (a) The Heretic
   (b) The Spawning
   (c) The Final Insult
   (d) Electric Boogaloo

4) What essential plot difference did Sigourney Weaver insist on before agreeing to appear in Alien^3?

5) How did Jack Palance re-appear in City Slickers II after his character Curly was killed off in the original?

6) Mahoney, Lassard, Hightower, Tackleberry are all characters from which franchise?

7) What was the American title of Mad Max 2?

8) Which British science fiction novelist wrote the screenplay for Halloween 3: Season Of The Witch but asked to have his name taken off the end credits?

9) Robert Shaw, Edward Fox and Harrison Ford star in the sequel to a classic war movie. Can you name the original and its offspring?

10) Who played the title role in Robocop 3?

11) Which song are Wayne and Garth forced into performing during Wayne's World 2?

12) Beneath, Escape, Conquest and Battle are the prefixes for sequels to which 1968 film?

13) Name three items served to Kate Capshaw during the banquet scene in Indiana Jones And The Temple Of Doom.

14) Name the aircraft named in the subtitle of the fourth Airport movie.

15) Who or what is Porky's in the series of lame-brained comedies?

16) Who played Jeff Goldblum's offspring in The Fly 2?

17) Which of the following films *never* spawned a sequel; American Graffiti, The Sting, The Birds, Casper?

18) What did Marty McFly tell everyone his name was in Back To The Future: Part 3?

19) 'Thank God For Site B'. Name the sequel.

20) How many Nightmare On Elm Street sequels have there been and can you name the subtitles?

*Arnold Schwarzenegger's catchphrase from The Terminator that has become part of every day speech

The Empire 10

With a nod and a wink to Magnus Magnusson, welcome to the 'specialist subject round'. Here we test your knowledge on nine films and one 80s institution that, if you read Empire, you should know with a back-of-the-hand intimacy. Some are movies you've probably loved for yonks, others are recent additions to the flicks you shout about – either way, they are the films you watch every time they're on telly, quote from endlessly and are always in contention when compiling those all important top ten lists. The range of movies to choose from is endless – after all, Empire is an incredibly broad church – so unfortunately there is no space for the mystery of Keyser Soze, the bile of Withnail, the number 11 of Nigel Tufnel or the Hawaiian shirts of Nice Guy Eddie. But, for now, how much do you really know about these timeless Empire generation classics...?

'Everybody be cool. This is a robbery...'*

Pulp Fiction

1) What is the name of the 50s themed diner where Mia Wallace (Uma Thurman) takes Vincent Vega (John Travolta) on their date?

2) Who played the following characters?
   (a) Honey Bunny
   (b) Fabienne
   (c) Lance
   (d) Zed
   (e) Jimmie

3) What is Tony Rocky Horror's real name?

4) Which US sit-com saw Tarantino star in a lampoon of Pulp?

5) What flavour pancake does Fabienne tell Butch she is going to order?

6) Which pint sized actor part owns Jersey Films, the production company behind Pulp?

7) Who shared Pulp's Best Screenplay Oscar with Tarantino?

8) What is the chapter and verse of the biblical passage Jules has memorized?

9) What prize did Pulp nab at the Cannes Film Festival?

10) What is the name of Mia Wallace's character from the Fox Force Five TV pilot?

11) Who is the 50s American film director who lends his name to the steak ordered by Vincent Vega?

12) Michael Madsen turned down the role of Vincent Vega to join the cast of which film?

13) What brand of burger does Jules steal from Brett?

14) Which song plays over the sequence depicting Mia dancing around her apartment?

15) Where did Captain Koons (Christopher Walken) hide the gold watch for two years before presenting it to Butch?

16) What did Samuel L. Jackson famously mutter to a world wide audience on losing the Best Supporting Actor Oscar to Martin Landau?

17) Which song plays over the front credits and who performs it?

18) Which character does Steve Buscemi play?

19) In 'The Bonnie Situation' segment, what is Bonnie's profession?

20) Why is a quarter pounder in France called a Royale with Cheese?

*Line delivered by Pumpkin (Tim Roth) to attract punters' attention

43

'Wake up, time to die...' *

Blade Runner

1) What is the name of Sean Young's character?

2) Name the author and title of the book upon which Blade Runner is based.

3) Where and when is Blade Runner set?

4) Who wrote the film's score?

5) What is the name of the organization responsible for creating replicants?

6) Who portrays the following replicants?
   (a) Roy Batty
   (b) Leon
   (c) Zhora
   (d) Pris

7) What links Blade Runner with the Unforgiven?

8) Which animal is present when Harrison Ford first meets Sean Young?

9) Finish this classic voiceover: 'I don't know how long we'd have together...'

10) What variety act is Zhora performing?

11) What year was Blade Runner released?

12) What is the euphemism for execution used when a Blade Runner kills a replicant?

13) What is Deckard's Christian name?

14) What is the name of the smoke used to give the film its distinctive look?

15) Who or what are Spinners?

16) Name three differences between the The Director's Cut and the original version.

17) What slang term does police chief Bryant used to describe replicants?

18) Who plays JF Sebastiane?

19) What does Gaff leave outside the door of Deckard's apartment?

20) The final aerial shots are culled from the rushes of which horror film?

*Line delivered by Batty in the last throes of his life

'It's shite being Scottish...' *

Trainspotting

1) Name the frighteningly talented writer–director–producer trio behind Trainspotting.

2) Which character is played by author Irvine Welsh?

3) Which actor do Renton and Sick Boy mimic when lining up the small dog with an air rifle?

4) What is Begbie's Christian name?

5) Which moment of Scottish footballing history does Renton compare his sexual state of mind to?

6) What bombshell does Diane drop on Renton the morning after their night of passion?

7) Who performs the following Trainspotting anthems?
    (a) Lust For Life
    (b) Perfect Day
    (c) Mile End
    (d) Born Slippy

8) In what category was Trainspotting nominated for an Oscar and what did it lose out to?

9) Who plays Sick Boy?

10) In the opening monologue, what are the first three things Renton 'chooses'?

11) Apart from Trainspotting, name three other films Ewan McGregor appeared in during 1996?

12) Which opera is playing over the sequence of Renton going cold turkey?

13) What are the girls talking about when questioned by Spud and Tommy in the club?

14) Which big name sequel did the team turn down in the aftermath of Trainspotting?

15) Name the game show host who turns up in Renton's nightmare.

16) Apart from Ewan McGregor, name the other actor who appears in both Shallow Grave and Trainspotting?

17) What area of employment does Spud attempt to enter in a disastrous job interview?

18) What certificate did Trainspotting receive?

19) Which song is playing when Diane first meets Renton?

20) Finish off the following Trainspotting pearl of wisdom: 'One day, there won't be men or women...'?

*Line delivered by Renton (Ewan McGregor) whilst experiencing the pleasures of the countryside

'Summer lovin' happened so fast…'*

Grease

1) Who directed Grease?

2) Name John Travolta's character.

3) Name the school in which Grease is set.

4) According to the song's lyrics, who is 'lousy with virginity' ?

5) Who plays Kenickie?

6) Who wrote the original stage musical on which the film is based?

7) What is the name of John Travolta's gang and their rivals?

8) What is Rizzo's Christian name?

9) Which of the songs was nominated for an Academy Award?

10) Name the four sports Travolta tries out in order to become a jock.

11) What links Grease with the Pink Panther series?

12) Which role does Sid Caesar play?

13) Name the musical Olivia Newton John made with Gene Kelly in 1980.

14) Who sings Beauty School Drop-Out?

15) What three adjectives does Travolta use to describe the car in the prelude to Greased Lightning?

16) Name the TV show that hosts the dancing competition? For an extra point name the slimy presenter.

17) Name the location of the high speed race.

18) Which songs do the following lyrics come from?
   a) 'You better shape up, 'cause I need a man…'
   b) 'The chicks'll cream…'
   c) 'Like, does he have a car?…aha'
   d) 'This is a life of illusion…'
   e) 'What will they say, Monday at school…'

19) Apart from Rizzo, name three other Pink Ladies.

20) Name the two stars of Grease 2.

*Line warbled by Olivia Newton John in Summer Nights song

'You're gonna need a bigger boat…' *

Jaws

1) Jaws starred the inimitable troika of Robert Shaw, Roy Scheider and Richard Dreyfuss: character names please?

2) Name the town where Jaws is set and the Island which served as the location.

3) Jaws features a famous Dolly Zoom effect borrowed from which Hitchcock film?

4) Who composed the famous 'der-dum, der-dum' theme tune?

5) Name the film starring Goldie Hawn that Steven Spielberg had completed prior to starting Jaws?

6) What was the nickname given to the mechanical shark by Spielberg? For extra kudos, who designed the special effects shark?

7) Who plays Roy Scheider's wife?

8) What cameo role does Jaws author Peter Benchley take?

9) How does Robert Shaw attract the attention of the quickly assembled council meeting?

10) What species of shark is the title star?

12) Name the torpedoed ship which features in Robert Shaw's chilling justification for never wearing a life jacket.

13) Who was originally set for Robert Shaw's role but opted out for tax reasons?

14) During the late night autopsy scene, the number plate retrieved from the Shark's innards is from which state?

15) In a famous Jaws moment Robert Shaw crushes a beer can in one hand. What is Richard Dreyfuss' riposte?

16) What is the name of Robert Shaw's boat?

17) Which studio theme park contains the Jaws-related attraction?

18) Which song do Shaw, Scheider and Dreyfuss sing after an onboard drinking session?

19) Which Peter Benchley novel, also with an aquatic theme, was filmed in 1977, also starring Robert Shaw?

20) How does Roy Scheider finally see off the malevolent fish?

*Memorable utterance from Roy Scheider on catching first sight of the shark

'Don't call me Shirley…'*

Airplane

1) Name the trio behind Airplane.

2) What links Airplane to science fiction classic Forbidden Planet?

3) Who plays Ted Striker?

4) What are the addictions that Captain McCroskey (Lloyd Bridges) is trying to give up?

5) What two dishes are on the flight's menu?

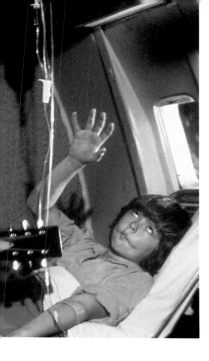

6) Which author is jokily referred to in the end credits?

7) Where is the flight's destination?

8) What is the name of the lieutenant who lost his life under Striker's command?

9) Peter Graves, who plays Captain Oveur, was the star of which seminal 60s TV series?

10) Which Broadway legend features in the psychiatric hospital sequence?

11) Name the two 'zones' that are argued over in the opening sequence.

12) Which film is parodied in Ted and Elaine's flashback beachside romp?

13) Answer the following question in classic Airplane style: 'A Hospital? What is it?'

14) Which famous basketball star cameos as one of the cockpit crew?

15) Elaine is one air hostess on the flight. Name the other?

16) As listed in the credits, what is the name of the inflatable co-pilot?

17) What year did Airplane come out?

18) What is unusual about the Air Israel flight?

19) Julie Hagerty, who plays Elaine, stars in which Woody Allen film?

20) What was the tragedy-stricken vehicle at the centre of Airplane II: The Sequel?

*Leslie Nielsen misunderstands the word 'surely' to classic comic effect

'The force will be with you…always' *

The Star Wars Trilogy

1) What are the legendary, fairytale-like words that precede all three films?

2) What are the only other feature films that George Lucas has directed?

3) If Star Wars was conceived as a nine part saga, which episode number is the film Star Wars and what is its subheading?

4) What species of alien is Chewbacca?

5) Which country provided the location for Tatooine in the first Star Wars?

6) What is the name of the character Peter Cushing played?

7) What is Luke's call sign during the attack on the first Death Star?

8) Name the legendary special effects company set up by George Lucas specifically for Star Wars.

9) What was Princess Leia's home planet?

10) Which Star Wars character features as a nightclub moniker in Indiana Jones And The Temple Of Doom?

11) Name three other films Mark Hamill has appeared in, apart from the Star Wars trilogy.

12) Where is the cantina in which Luke and Ben Kenobi first meet Han Solo?

13) Which Star Wars parody features characters called Dark Helmet and Pizza The Hutt?

14) Name the now big name director who worked as a special effects technician on Return Of The Jedi.

15) Who or what links Star Wars to Local Hero?

16) Who provides the voice for Yoda?

17) Name the two actors who portrayed The Emperor in The Empire Strikes Back and Return Of The Jedi.

18) Complete the following Star Wars dialogue: 'Travelling through hyperspace…'

19) Name the only actor ever to be Oscar nominated for a Star Wars film.

20) What is the significance of the phrase 'Blue Harvest' in relation to the Star Wars films?

*Advice from Obi-Wan Kenobi (Sir Alec Guinness) to Luke Skywalker (Mark Hamill)

'Keep your friends close and your
enemies closer...' *

The Godfather Trilogy

1) Name Vito Corleone's four children.

2) Who wrote the novel upon which the film is based?

3) Which actress dropped out of The Godfather Part III due to ill health?

4) Which character was shot in the eye towards the end of The Godfather Part 1?

5) Complete the following line of classic Godfather dialogue: 'Fredo, you're my older brother...'

6) Name the two composers of the films' music.

7) Outside of The Godfather trilogy, name the other gangster-themed film directed by Francis Ford Coppola?

8) Who or what is a *consigliere*?

9) How did Appolonia die?

10) Whose child is baptised at the end of The Godfather Part I?

11) What is the family's legitimate business?

12) Name the 1990 film which saw Brando parody his Godfather role.

13) What is the opening line of the first film?

14) Who plays Hyman Roth?

15) What is the name of the singer whom the Don helps using a horse's head?

16) Which film is playing during Michael and Kay's New York shopping spree?

17) Name the characters played by the following;
    (a) Andy Garcia
    (b) Richard Conte
    (c) Sterling Hayden
    (d) Robert Duvall
    (e) Joe Mantegna

18) Name the producer of The Godfather who was also married to Ali MacGraw.

19) What did Vito have in his mouth when he died?

20) In Godfather-speak, what is meant by the term 'go to the mattresses'?

*Wise words from Frankie Pentangeli (Michael V. Gazzo)

'We're on a mission from God…' *

The Blues Brothers

1) Who directed The Blues Brothers?

2) Which American TV institution did The Blues Brothers characters debut on?

3) Name the items handed back to Jake by the prison.

4) Which two songs do Jake and Elwood perform at the country and western club? For an extra point, name the song they start but do not finish.

5) Which two other films have also paired John Belushi and Dan Aykroyd?

6) Which Elvis Presley song is featured in the final scene?

7) What is the solitary line of dialogue spoken in the car as the 'Illinois Nazis' plummet to the ground?

8) What is the name of the country and western band ousted by The Blues Brothers to play Bob's Country Bunker?

9) What does Jake order in Aretha Franklin's diner?

10) Name three ways Carrie Fisher tries to bump off John Belushi.

11) And what is her motive for trying to kill him?

12) Which legendary real life R'n'B band forms the nucleus of The Blues Brothers band?

13) Who plays Sister Mary Stigmata?

14) Complete the following Blues Brothers dialogue: 'It's a hundred and six miles to Chicago...'

15) How much do Jake and Elwood have to raise to save the orphanage?

16) Which model does Dan Aykroyd meet at the petrol station?

17) What is the only time Belushi removes his glasses in the whole film?

18) Who sings the following songs:
   (a) Think
   (b) Minnie The Moocher
   (c) That Old Landmark
   (d) Shake Your Tailfeather

19) Where does the phrase 'See You Next Wednesday' appear and what is its significance?

20) What is the last line spoken in the film and who delivers it?

*Delivered by Elwood Blues (Dan Aykroyd) to convince doubters of his good intentions

'You're a neo-maxi zoom dweebie...' *

The Brat Pack

1) The phrase Brat Pack is a pun on which clique of 60s swingers and singers?

2) Name the seven Brat Packers who make up the cast for St. Elmo's Fire.

3) Which writer/director/producer is the creative force behind most Brat Pack movies?

4) Name the musical artists behind the following Brat Pack showstoppers:
   (a) Don't You Forget About Me
   (b) Man In Motion (Theme from St. Elmo's Fire)
   (c) Pretty In Pink

5) What is the name of Jon Cryer's character in Pretty In Pink?

6) An early incarnation of the Brat Pack can be found in The Outsiders. Who wrote the novel upon which the film is based?

7) Name the film which pitched Molly Ringwald with nerdy Anthony Michael Hall before The Breakfast Club.

8) Who plays Molly Ringwald's father in Pretty in Pink?

9) St. Elmo's Fire: which Brat Pack member has a cocaine habit?

10) What is the 'going away present' that Mare Winningham gives Rob Lowe in the same film?

11) In Pretty in Pink, which song plays over the sequence where Molly Ringwald makes her prom dress?

12) Who plays the object of Emilio Estevez's affection in St. Elmo's Fire?

13) What movie theme tune do The Breakfast Club whistle whilst in detention?

14) In St. Elmo's Fire, what unusual type of container does Andrew McCarthy use to attract women?

15) Who played the dream woman in Weird Science?

16) Name the director of St. Elmo's Fire and the two superhero movies which he has directed.

17) Who or what links Pretty In Pink to Crash?

18) Which Brat Packers can be found in the following post 'Pack' films?
    (a) Wayne's World
    (b) Mission: Impossible
    (c) Weekend At Bernie's
    (d) Fandango
    (e) A Few Good Men

19) What special method does Molly Ringwald use to apply lipstick in The Breakfast Club?

20) What is a St. Elmo's Fire?

*Bad boy John Bender (Judd Nelson) pastes nerd Brian Johnson (Anthony Michael Hall) with an unintelligible insult in The Breakfast Club

Picture Round

A helpless businesman is strafed by a crop-dusting bi-plane. A boxer dances round the ring in mesmerizing black-and-white. A child's bike flies over a storybook moon. Classic visual moments such as these are lodged in moviegoers' brains forever. To celebrate the power and primacy of the cinematic image, keep 'em peeled for this selection of picture led posers.

'OK boys let's get some pictures…' *

▶ 1) Name the film about the character played by Mel Gibson.

2) Who played his wife in the film?

3) What links this film with cult TV series The

◀ 4) Name the film and the actor.

5) What is the vocation of this character?

6) Under what circumstances was this actor famously jailed for 50 days?

▶ 7) Name the film and the actor under all the make-up.

8) Madonna also features in the film. Can you name her character?

9) Which legendary cinematographer provided the startling look for the film?

10) What links the above three films?

Name these superstars of the future who appear in these embarrassing childhood snaps.

◀ 11) *Clue:* this little cherub grew up to be a serial killer and a corrupt president.

▲ 12) *Clue:* this blue-eyed blond has been a cowboy, a cardshark and a randy millionaire.

◀ 13) *Clue:* this time-traveller-to-be knows a thing or two about flogging hamburgers.

14) Can you name the grown-ups who played kids in the following films?
  (a) Jack
  (b) Big
  (c) Vice Versa
  (d) Like Father, Like Son

15) Who is this? For extra kudos, can you also name the film?

16) Who is his real life wife?

17) Who is this beauty? What is the full title of the film?

18) Name the two other stars.

19) Name the film and the usually serious thesp with the neck difficulties.

20) Which Tennessee Williams play provides the basis for the musical which opens this film?

*The shout of the press pack from Airplane as they remove photographs from the wall

The Quirky Zone

Welcome to the zone they call 'quirky', a section where anything and everything goes. From the dialogue that kickstarts movies to the films that should have never been made, be prepared to have the width and depth of your film knowledge well and truly tested. The rules are... there aren't any rules...

'Ready? Yeah, boot it…' *

Opening Lines

The first words uttered in a movie. It's a make or break decision for any scriptwriter wishing to engage an audience immediately. Can you remember the films that contain these opening salvoes?

1) 'Chapter one. He adored New York. He idolized it out of all proportion.'

2) 'For nearly forty years this story has given faithful service to the young in heart and time has been powerless to put its kindly philosophy out of fashion.'

3) 'Last night I dreamed I went to Manderley again.'

4) 'In the old days, I remember a wind that blowed down through the canyon. It was a hot wind called Santana and it carried with it the smell of warm places.'

5) 'I'm not ashamed. I've known love. I've known rejection. I'm not afraid to declare my feelings. Take trust, for instance, or friendship.'

6) 'What can you say about a 25-year old girl who died? That she was beautiful and brilliant. That she loved Mozart and Bach. And The Beatles. And me.'

7) 'I'm going for a cup of tea… D'you want one?'

8) 'All right, everyone…this is a stick up! Don't anybody move!'

9) 'I never knew the old Vienna before the war with its Strauss music, its glamour and easy charm.'

10) 'Alright, Charlie. That the joint?'

11) 'To sin by silence when we should protest makes cowards out of men.' (This is on a titlecard – not spoken.)

12) 'The Hovitos are near. The poison is still fresh…three days. They're following us.'

13) 'You don't make up for your sins in Church. You do it in the streets. You do it at home. The rest is all bullshit and you know it.'

14) 'Saigon… shit.'

15) 'There was a land of Cavaliers and cotton fields called the Old South.'

16) 'Harry, answer that. So whaddya wanna hack for Bickle?'

17) 'Action man patrol, fall in! Hold your fire until I give the order!'

18) 'In 1539 the Knights Templar of Malta paid tribute to Charles V of Spain by sending him a Golden Falcon encrusted with rarest jewels… But pirates seized the galley carrying this priceless token…'

19) 'On November 1 1959, the population of New York City was 8,042,783. If you laid all these people end to end, figuring an average height of five feet six- and-a-half inches, they would reach from Times Square to the outskirts of Karachi, Pakistan.'

20) 'This is the story of an unprejudiced heart…'

*Opening line from Strange Days (1996)

'Just when you thought it was safe to go back in the water…' *

Taglines

They adorn movie posters like war medals. They all sound like they should be read in a deep gravelly voice. They are the taglines – the hook designed to entice the audience into parting with their hard earned cash. Your mission – should you choose to accept it – is to identify the films summed up by the following capsule descriptions.

1) 'His whole life life was a million to one shot.'

2) 'I race cars. I play tennis. I fondle women. But I have weekends off and I am my own boss.'

3) 'Man is the warmest place to hide.'

4) 'There's a herd of killer rabbits heading this way!'

5) 'Creepy. Kooky. Spooky. Ooky.'

6) 'A great guy with his chopper!'

7) 'What one loves about life are the things that fade.'

8) 'Protecting the Earth from the scum of the universe.'

9) 'Don't get mad. Get everything.'

10) 'They're young… they're in love and they kill people.'

11) 'You like to watch, don't you?'

12) 'It's not over… it's not over.'

13) 'Where were you in '62?'

14) 'Flesh seduces. Passion kills.'

15) 'Mean. Green. And on the screen.'

16) 'We are not alone…'

17) 'Not that it matters, but most of it is true!'

18) 'From a place you may have never heard of, a story you'll never forget…'

19) 'Trust me, I'm a doctor.'

20) 'No sex. No booze. No men. No way!'

*Perhaps the most mimicked tagline of all: Jaws 2 (1978)

'Weird on top and wild at heart…' *

Cult Movies

Bloodcurdling violence, the kinkiest sex and and a no-holds-barred desire to go over the edge at every opportunity. No, not the House Of Commons but the dark and dangerous universe of cult movies – that subgenre of films that leads you down paths other movies are just too scared to tread. Exciting, challenging and occasionally downright bonkers, the world of cultdom is now awaiting your perusal. Enter at your peril…

1) 'It's just a jump to the left and a step to the right…' Instructions to which dance in which cult classic?

2) What did Divine famously eat at the end of Pink Flamingoes? For a bonus point name the film's director?

3) Who is Roderick Jaynes in relation to the Coen Brothers films?

4) Name the cult film-maker behind Bad Taste, Braindead and The Frighteners.

5) Sam Lowry is the lead character in which cult movie?

6) Who or what links Quadrophenia to Men Behaving Badly?

7) Can you answer the following questions on cult masterpiece Apocalypse Now?
   (a) Name the song that plays over the opening scenes of napalm destruction.
   (b) Which actor did Martin Sheen replace after only one week of filming?
   (c) Which piece of classical music does Robert Duvall play from his helicopters whilst flying into battle?
   (d) Name the renowned making-of Apocalypse Now documentary.

8) Why is it no longer possible to see A Clockwork Orange in the UK?

9) Name the production company behind such cheapjack ventures as The Toxic Adventure, Chopper Chicks In Zombietown and The Class Of Nuke 'Em High.

10) What is the better known title for cult French movie 37.2 Degrees Au Matin?

11) What is unusual about Winona Ryder's participation in the croquet game that opens Heathers?

12) 'People say all kinds of crazy shit during sex. One time I called this girl mom…' Name the film.

13) Which innocuous mode of transport is the linchpin for a horrific drive-by shooting in Assault On Precinct 13?

14) Which movie features a 'Scooby Doo philosopher' in its end credits?

15) The Naked Lunch is based on the writings of which cult icon?

16) Twelve Monkeys is based on which short French movie? Can you also name the directors of both films?

17) Who plays the title role in Henry: Portrait Of A Serial Killer?

18) Who directed Faster Pussycat, Kill!, Kill! and Vixen?

19) Which DIY tool would you most readily associate with Abel Ferrara?

20) In which David Lynch films would you find;
    (a) Nicolas Cage crooning Elvis
    (b) John Hurt under layers of make up
    (c) Sting in a codpiece
    (d) David Bowie as an FBI Agent
    (e) Dennis Hopper inhaling gas for kicks?

*Lulu's (Laura Dern) worldview in Wild At Heart (1990)

'Let's get into character…' *

The Name Game

Luke Skywalker, Indiana Jones and Buzz Lightyear. Some character monikers just stick in the memory. Others, however, might prove to be a bit more slippery. Who played the following characters and in which films?

1) Catherine Trammell

2) Mars Blackmon

3) Veronica Sawyer

4) George Bailey

5) Hildy Johnson

6) Ellie Sattler

7) H.I. McDonough

8) Lisa Carol Fremont

9) Vincent Hanna

10) Matty Walker

11) Beverly and Elliott Mantle (clue: *it's one actor*)

12) Fielding Melish

13) Bree Daniels

14) Gordon Gekko

15) Marion Crane

16) Joe Buck

17) Laurie Strode

18) Dr Richard Kimble

19) Tina Carlyle

20) Kevin McCallister

*Line from Jules (Samuel L. Jackson) to Vincent (John Travolta) in Pulp Fiction 1994

'If you want art, don't mess around with movies. Buy a Picasso…' *

Shite!

Some films are born great. Some films have greatness thrust upon them. Others are just monumentally rubbish. How well do you know the films from which you could have rightfully demanded your money back?

....

1) Can you pick out the notoriously useless films from the following descriptions?
    (a) A salvage operation on a famous shipwreck
    (b) A computer falls in love with its owner
    (c) Paul Hogan is a born again saint
    (d) Bruce Willis is a cat burglar who can carry a tune
    (e) Julia Roberts falls for a leukaemia victim

2) Who wrote the book on which mega-flop The Bonfire Of The Vanities was based?

3) Which actress had an early role opposite the distinctly mechanical 1976 King Kong?

4) Who plays Crêpe Suzette in which Brit-flop?

5) What fashion item is pivotal to the plot of London Kills Me?

6) Who played the two songwriters in Ishtar?

7) What film was dubbed 'Fishtar' during its troubled production?

8) Who portrayed Ed Wood Jr, the world's worst film director, in the 1996 biopic? For extra brownie points name three films Ed Wood directed.

9) Which (at that time) married couple starred in Shanghai Surprise?

10) In Look Who's Talking Now, who or what got to vocalize their thoughts? And who or what provided the voices?

11) Who played Supergirl in the 1984 stinker?

12) Who or what links the débâcle of Four Rooms with the débâcle of late night TV show The Word?

13) Describe the premise of Boxing Helena. Can you also name the director and her famous father?

14) Which pop singer had a small role in the disastrous civil war epic Revolution?

15) Which 1981 flop featured a waterskiing elephant?

16) What was the subtitle that adorned Howard The Duck?

17) What is the name of the awards ceremony – held the night before the Oscars – that celebrates non-achievement in film?

18) George Burns, Frankie Howerd, Donald Pleasence, Paul Nicholas, Alice Cooper and Steve Martin starred in which 1978 musical clunker?

19) Name the producer – renowned for his disaster epics – behind the 1978 turkey The Swarm.

20) 'Ladies and gentlemen…The girl to tickle your pickle!' Name both the film and the screenwriter responsible for such cringeworthy dialogue.

*Film-making philosophy of Michael Winner

'And that's all I have to say about that…' *

Closing Lines

The butt of the villain has been kicked. The lips of the heroine have been kissed. The only thing left to do is to leave the audience with a parting shot so memorable that it will recur in pub conversations for years to come. Can you place the films which these lasting last lines come from?

1) 'I'm an average nobody. I get to live the rest of my life like a schnook.'

2) 'Madness! Madness!'

3) 'It was beauty killed the beast.'

4) 'Just like that he's gone.'

5) 'The old man was right, only the farmers won. We lost. We'll always lose.'

6) 'I agree with the second part.'

7) 'I never had any friends later on like the ones I had when I was twelve. Jesus, did anyone?'

8) 'Where are you guys goin'? Wait a minute! I'll be back! And I'll remember every last one of ya!'

9) 'I hope they are watching. They'll see, they'll see and they'll know. And they'll say, "why she wouldn't even harm a fly".'

10) 'I think I'll have a drink.'

11) 'There is a silence where no sound may be, in the cold grave under the deep, deep sea.'

12) 'Throw that junk.'

13) 'That's my girl. And that's my boy.'

14) 'All right Mr De Mille, I'm ready for my close up now.'

15) 'Dennis will like that. I must remember to tell him.'

16) 'We took a secret vote. We're not leaving. We're never leaving.'

17) 'No, I'd only blow it.'

18) 'Bugger it. I meant to say "Cheerio".'

19) 'He did. He ran them off their feet.'

20) 'Hey, I'm back.'

*Forrest Gump's inimitable way of closing a subject

'Be afraid. Be very afraid…' *

Bloody Hard

You may know John Wayne's real name. You possibly know who played The Magnificent Seven. But these standard teasers can be found in the file marked 'easy-peasy-lemon-squeezy' compared to the 20 hoops of film buffular fire you now have to jump through. Gird that noggin. Crank up the cranium. Only the fittest (saddest?) will make it through. Be careful, it's a jungle out there…

1) Name three actresses who have been directed by Steven Spielberg more than once.

2) Which film bore the working title Would I Lie To You?

3) Name five directors who have had a cameo in John Landis movies.

4) Who played the following unscrupulous journos and in which films?
   (a) J J Hunsecker
   (b) Chuck Tatum
   (c) Waldo Lydecker

5) What links The Godfather, All The President's Men and Annie Hall?

6) Before Schindler's List, what was the last black-and-white film to win a Best Picture Oscar?

7) Who played call sign 'Merlin' in Top Gun?

8) Which big name directors made the following early short films?
   (a) It's Not Just You Murray
   (b) Field Of Honour
   (c) Joe's Bed-Stuy Barbershop: We Cut Heads
   (d) Passionless Moments

9) Who or what links Richard Gere with Japanese maestro Akira Kurosawa?

10) What is meant by the term 'aspect ratio'?

11) The prison conclusion of American Gigolo is a reference to which classic French film?

12) Four Weddings And A Funeral: what number do you get if you add the amount of lovers Carrie (Andie MacDowell) has devoured to the amount Charlie (Hugh Grant) admits to?

13) Who invented popcorn?

14) Name the three directors who have made versions of Jack Kinney's The Body Snatchers story.

15) In which filmic field are Rick Baker and Rob Bottin leading exponents?

16) Which *enfant terrible* famously said the following: 'Cinema is far too rich and capable a medium to be merely left to the storytellers.'?

17) Which song plays over the front credits of Benny and Joon?

18) The name of Quentin Tarantino's production company is a pun on the title of which film by French New Waver Jean-Luc Godard?

19) Name three films directed by Michael Crichton.

20) Name the 35 Classic Disney full length animated feature films.

*Tagline for the Fly remake (1986)

'Teamwork is everybody doing what I say' *

Team Games

Here's the deal: the dessert has been polished off, the beverages quaffed and the what-we-did-on-our-holiday stories are out of the way. You've even flirted with the friend of a friend who always turns up on these occasions. The only ritual left to observe is the after dinner game. What better way to round off a convivial evening than some movie-related group quizzes. Best of all, they don't involve a board, dice or any arguments about forking out 400 quid when you land on Park Lane.

SIX DEGREES OF KEVIN BACON

The object of the game is to name any currently living – or, if you're feeling confident, dead – actor or director and then try to link them back to the prodigious Kevin in six moves or fewer. Actors and directors are linked together either by sharing the same credit space or by shiftier means (e.g. familial connections) to create a family tree-style lineage building up to the one and only Kevmeister. For example:

AL PACINO TO KEVIN BACON:
AL PACINO starred in City Hall with BRIDGET FONDA who starred in Single White Female with JENNIFER JASON LEIGH who starred in The Big Picture with KEVIN BACON.

Or

CLINT EASTWOOD TO KEVIN BACON:
CLINT EASTWOOD starred in In The Line Of Fire with RENE RUSSO who starred in Get Shorty which featured a cameo by BETTE MIDLER who starred in Scenes From A Mall with WOODY ALLEN who directed Hannah And Her Sisters starring DIANNE WIEST who starred in Footloose with – hey! – KEVIN BACON.

*Team dynamics courtesy of Hollywood mogul Sam Goldwyn

Get the picture? Divide yourselves into teams to see who can bring home the bacon first. Have a go at these before coming up with your own Kevin conundrums. Solutions on page 109.

ROBIN WILLIAMS
SIR ALEC GUINNESS
MERYL STREEP
70s Sitcom star JOHN ALDERTON
TOMMY LEE JONES

ALPHABET SOUP

Starting with A, the idea is to work through the alphabet, with each player coming up with an actor, actress or director whose surname begins with the requisite letter. Each player has only fifteen seconds to dredge their memories for a suitable candidate. Failure to come up with a name means an agreed forfeit of some kind (remove a piece of clothing, listen to a Rick Astley album, etc). If a player can come up with a double whammy in which Christian and surname begin with the same letters (e.g. Alan Alda, Brigitte Bardot, Charlie Chaplin, etc) then he can forgo a later forfeit, if necessary. Some help with 'tricky' letters can be found on page 110.

from Alda…

…to Zemeckis

BUFF OR BUFFOON

Or how to show off your astonishing movie knowledge and fall out with friends, all at the same time.

STARTING THE GAME

1. You need at least four players – or more if you want to show off your high rating in the popularity stakes.

2. Each player chooses seven (count 'em) of their favourite films. In the name of fair play and decency these should be films that everyone has heard of – choosing the 1932 Japanese classic Mito Komon or the top shelf masterpiece Big, Bad And Bouncy, is just not cricket.

3. Each player writes their faves down on a piece of paper. The lists are then put together, ruthlessly mocked ('The Railway Children! Ha!') and any duplicates removed. (The maximum number of films would therefore be 28, but a typical game would consist of 16)

4. Each player in turn – Ladies firsts, gents, to prove that chivalry is not dead – will choose a film from the list and attempt to score points by showing off their knowledge of it.

THE EASY, MEDIUM OR HARD SCORING SYSTEM

Points are scored according to the depth of knowledge displayed. Each player must nominate how many points he intends to try for.

1. Easy: Score one point for any piece of trivia considered a doddle, for example, naming a character or describing a scene.
2. Medium: Score *deux* points for something that's a little bit tougher, such as quoting a well known line of dialogue. Remember, though, once a player has quoted this line it cannot be repeated by another player.
3. Hard: Scoring three points is the ultimate challenge. Here a player must quote a piece of extended dialogue from a film, or surprise players with a piece of dazzlingly original info on the film (a true one if you please).

THE RULES

1. The winner is the one with the most points once everyone has answered a question on each film on the list.
2. Every player can score (one, two or three) points on each film, but only once, so time your choices well.
3. All disputes should be settled by general consensus which should in no way be affected by the quantity of booze quaffed. And remember – as they say at every Olympics – it's not the winning that counts, it's the taking part. Yeah, right.

Answers

Answers

GENRE

ANIMATION

1. Cruella De Vil
2. Anime
3. The Rescuers Down Under
4. John Lasseter
5. Anchors Aweigh
6. (a) Mel Blanc (c) George Sanders (d) Kathleen Turner
   (d) Robin Williams (e) Demi Moore
7. Bambi
8. Aardman Animation
9. Bill Murray
10. Ray Harryhausen
11. William Hanna and Joseph Barbera
12. Tim Burton
13. Yellow Submarine
14. Dougal And The Blue Cat
15. Ralph Bakshi
16. (a) The Jungle Book (b) Pinocchio (c) Song Of The South
    (d) Beauty And The Beast (e) Toy Story
17. James Earl Jones – provides the voice of the titular monarch and Darth Vader.
18. Bashful, Sleepy, Grumpy, Sneezy, Happy, Doc and Dopey
19. Fantasia
20. Porky Pig

SCIENCE FICTION

1. Nostromo
2. David Bowie
3. 2001: A Space Odyssey
4. The body of another scientist
5. He designed and built the title star
6. (a) Forbidden Planet (b) The Day The Earth Stood Still (c) Silent Running
   (d) The Black Hole (e) Short Circuit

7. Amazing Grace
8. Sil
9. Sleeper
10. The Thing From Another World
11. H.G. Wells
12. 'Aha…Saviour of the Universe!'
13. Barbarella
14. Steve McQueen
15. Morphing
16. Will Smith in Independence Day
17. (a) Fritz Lang (b) John Boorman (d) David Lynch (d) John McTiernan
    (e) Barry Sonnenfeld
18. Dark Star
19. Jeff Bridges
20. First is a sighting of a UFO; second is physical evidence left by a UFO

JAMES BOND

1. Author Ian Fleming
2. Sean Connery – Dr No, David Niven – Casino Royale, George Lazenby – On Her Majesty's Secret Service, Roger Moore – Live And Let Die, Timothy Dalton – The Living Daylights, Pierce Brosnan – Goldeneye
3. Because it was felt American audiences would not know the meaning of the word 'revoked'
4. Felix Leiter
5. 1 = c; 2 = e; 3 = d ; 4 = a; 5 = b
6. Special Executive for Counter-Intelligence, Terrorism, Revenge and Extortion
7. Sheena Easton in For Your Eyes Only
8. Richard Kiel. The Spy Who Loved Me and Moonraker
9. He has a third nipple
10. Mr. Wint and Mr. Kidd
11. Tanya Roberts, who played Stacey in A View To A Kill
12. A volcano
13. Albert R. 'Cubby' Brocolli
14. '…No Mr Bond, I expect you to die!'
15. Octopussy – On Her Majesty's Secret Service was an instrumental
16. Never Say Never Again
17. Charles Gray, Donald Pleasence, Telly Savalas
18. Pinewood

19. (a) The Spy Who Loved Me (b) You Only Live Twice (c) Moonraker
    (d) Diamonds Are Forever (e) Goldfinger
20. Woody Allen, Casino Royale

HORROR

1. The TV set
2. The Slaughtered Lamb
3. One, don't get him wet; two, keep him out of bright light and three, never feed him after midnight
4. Dario Argento
5. (a) Hellraiser (b) Friday The 13th (c) The Texas Chainsaw Massacre
    (d) Halloween
6. Mia Farrow and John Cassavetes
7. The Necronomicon
8. Hammer
9. Thorn
10. Robert Englund
11. Scanners, Videodrome, The Fly
12. William Peter Blatty
13. The Overlook
14. There are no women in it – except Kurt Russell's blow-up doll
15. Elsa Lanchester
16. Tod Browning
17. (a) Tom Hanks (b) Kevin Bacon (c) Matthew McConaughey
    (d) Leonardo DiCaprio
18. Carrie
19. She is a TV news reporter
20. Carry On Screaming

WESTERNS

1. Sergio Leone
2. Paul Newman and Robert Redford. Tom Berenger and William Katt
3. The name of the rollerskating rink
4. That'll Be The Day. The Searchers
5. Silverado
6. The Waco Kid
7. 'Rooster' Cogburn. True Grit
8. Do Not Forsake Me O My Darling

9. The Missouri Breaks
10. Mary McDonnell playing Stands With A Fist
11. Maverick
12. Fievel
13. John 'Doc' Holliday
14. The Wild Bunch
15. Monument Valley
16. William Munny
17. Madeleine Stowe, Drew Barrymore, Andie MacDowell, Mary Stuart Masterson
18. Wagons East!
19. Norman
20. The Good, The Bad And The Ugly

COMEDY
1. The Third Foot And Mouth Regiment
2. Aspen, Colorado
3. a = Four Weddings And a Funeral b = The Odd Couple
   c = Good Morning Vietnam d = The Naked Gun e = Ghostbusters
4. Ned Ryerson
5. He hands them a sample of pre-prepared child's urine
6. The Last Waltz
7. Cheech Marin and Tommy Chong
8. Alan Arkin
9. Snowflake
10. National Lampoon's Animal House
11. He's a driving instructor
12. Jacques Tati
13. The St. Valentine's Day Massacre
14. The Jerk
15. Alexander Mackendrick
16. The Gold Rush
17. 1 = c 2 = e 3 = d 4 = b 5 = a
18. Timothy Lea
19. Julius Marx
20. Bigguth Dickuth and Incontinentuth Buttockth

ANSWERS

MUSICALS

1. Irene Cara
2. Frederick Austerlitz and Virginia McMath
3. Pennies From Heaven
4. The Philadelphia Story
5. Gene Kelly, Debbie Reynolds, Donald O'Connor in Singin' In The Rain
6. Ken Russell
7. Diamonds Are A Girl's Best Friend. The Marilyn Monroe routine was parodied by Madonna in the promo video for Material Girl
8. The Jets and The Sharks
9. A brain, a heart and courage
10. Little Shop Of Horrors
11. Bob Fosse
12. Sky Masterson
13. I'll Say Anything
14. Meet Me In St Louis
15. Splurge guns
16. (a) A deer, a female deer (b) A drop of golden sun (c) A name I call myself
17. Busby Berkeley
18. 1 = c 2 = e 3 = d 4 = a 5 = b
19. Chitty Chitty Bang Bang
20. Jeff Goldblum, Jim Carrey and Damon Wayans

CHICK FLICKS

1. Leonardo DiCaprio and Claire Danes
2. Holly Golightly
3. Splendour In The Grass
4. 'Ditto'
5. Sam Neill and Harvey Keitel
6. An Affair To Remember. The Dirty Dozen
7. Now Voyager
8. I've Had The Time Of My Life. Bill Medley and Jennifer Warnes
9. a = Kelly McGillis b = Elisabeth Shue c = Renee Zellweger
   d = Mary Elizabeth Mastrantonio
10. Rock Hudson and Doris Day
11. Cello
12. Hector Elizondo
13. Four
14. Erich Segal

15. Ethan Hawke and Julie Delpy
16. David O. Selznick
17. Line up to hold her hair back
18. Richard Gere. Debra Winger. An Officer And A Gentleman
19. Maddison
20. 'I'll have what she's having!'

BLOCKBUSTERS

1. Keanu Reeves and Sandra Bullock in Speed
2. 76
3. Dean Devlin and Roland Emmerich
4. 1 = d 2 = a 3 = e 4 = c 5 = b
5. 88 miles per hour
6. 'You'll believe a man can fly'
7. Ray Parker Jr
8. Shane Black wrote Lethal Weapon and appears in Predator
9. Jack Nicholson in Batman (1989)
10. The headpiece left a burnt-in impression on the palm of Gestapo agent Toht during the blazing bar punch up in Nepal
11. The Hunt For Red October, Patriot Games, Clear And Present Danger. Alec Baldwin and Harrison Ford. Tom Clancy
12. Because Dorothy is the name of the character in The Wizard Of Oz, a film which begins with the mother of all tornadoes
13. John Lithgow
14. John
15. J. Lee Thompson
16. A chef
17. David Janssen
18. (a) Nakatomi Plaza (b) Hans Gruber (c) Bonnie Bedelia (d) Roy Rogers (e) He sticky tapes it to his back
19. The Channel Tunnel
20. Tyrannosaurus Rex, Velociraptor, Triceratops, Gallimimus, Brachiosaurus, Dilophosaurus

CRIME

1. Tony Montana
2. Brainerd
3. The Italian Job

4. 1 = c   2 = e   3 = b   4 = a   5 = d
5. The Taking Of Pelham 123
6. Double Indemnity
7. 'He sends one of yours to the hospital, you send one of his to the morgue. That's the Chicago way. And that's how you get Capone.'
8. It is absolutely silent
9. Raymond Chandler, Dashiell Hammett
10. Bob Hoskins, The Long Good Friday
11. Ford Mustang
12. Heat
13. His nose. Roman Polanski
14. Roy Budd
15. A hot cup of coffee
16. Bryan Singer
17. An ice pick
18. a) Jimmy 'The Gent' Conway (b) And Then He Kissed Me by The Crystals (c) Thelma Schoonmacher (d) Dances With Wolves (e) Paul Sorvino – who plays Paulie in GoodFellas – is the father of Mighty Aphrodite star Mira Sorvino.
19. 'Forget about it.'
20. (a) Warren Beatty and Faye Dunaway (b) Martin Sheen and Sissy Spacek
    (c) Keith Carradine and Shelley Duvall (d) Christian Slater and Patricia Arquette
    (e) Woody Harrelson and Juliette Lewis

HOLLYWOOD

THE ACADEMY AWARDS

1. It Happened One Night 1934; One Flew Over The Cuckoo's Nest 1975; The Silence Of The Lambs 1991
2. Kevin Spacey, The Usual Suspects
3. Katharine Hepburn, The Lion In Winter and Barbra Streisand, Funny Girl
4. The Godfather Part II
5. Lina Wertmuller, Seven Beauties and Jane Campion, The Piano
6. Linda Hunt in The Year Of Living Dangerously
7. Maggie Smith in California Suite
8. The Turning Point and The Color Purple
9. Geoffrey Rush for Shine
10. He was the streaker who raced behind David Niven at the 1973 ceremony
11. Close Encounters – it was nominated in the same year as Star Wars
12. Beauty And The Beast

13. Whoopi Goldberg and David Letterman
14. Sacheen Littlefeather, to highlight the plight of the Native American Indian. She was later revealed to be a professional actress named Maria Cruz
15. (a) Sally Field, Places In The Heart   (b) Tom Hanks, Forrest Gump
    (c) Mel Gibson, Braveheart   (d) Colin Welland, screenwriter, Chariots Of Fire
16. Eight hours
17. Seven
18. The Hustons: Walter and John Huston won for The Treasure Of The Sierra Madre and Anjelica Huston won for Prizzi's Honour
19. Irving J. Thalberg
20. Lyricist Oscar Hammerstein won gongs in 1941 and 1945

HOLLYWOOD COUPLES
1. 'Winona Forever'. 'Wino Forever'
2. (a) Kurt Russell and Goldie Hawn   (b) Laurence Olivier and Vivien Leigh
   (c) Demi Moore and Bruce Willis   (d) Meg Ryan and Dennis Quaid
   (e) Patricia Arquette and Nicolas Cage
3. Mimi Rogers
4. You're So Vain by Carly Simon
5. Amy Irving and Kate Capshaw
6. Hugh Grant and Liz Hurley – it is Grant's mugshot number following his arrest on Hollywood Boulevard
7. Gary Oldman – he's divorced them both
8. To Have And Have Not
9. Richard Gere and Cindy Crawford
10. Renny Harlin and Laura Dern
11. Vincente Minnelli
12. Via fax
13. Tony Curtis and Janet Leigh
14. He is 39 years her senior
15. Lyle Lovett
16. (a) Alec Baldwin and Kim Basinger   (b) Eric Stoltz and Bridget Fonda
    (c) Liam Neeson and Natasha Richardson   (d) Antonio Banderas and Melanie Griffith   (e) Kevin Kline and Phoebe Cates
17. Harrison Ford
18. Michael Keaton
19. Eight. In the grounds of Michael Jackson's mansion
20. Mae West

ANSWERS

DIRECTORS

1. Robert Zemeckis
2. The Scott Brothers – Ridley directed the former, Tony directed the latter
3. Video Archives
4. The Movie Brats
5. John Woo
6. *Rolling Stone*
7. Miami Vice
8. (a) John Singleton
   (b) Jan De Bont
   (c) Sir Richard Attenborough
   (d) Ed Burns
9. Richie Cunningham
10. Bigelow modelled clothes for The Gap
11. Robert Altman
12. Cartoons
13. David Wark
14. Oliver Stone
15. Alan Smithee is a pseudonym for any director who wishes to take his own name off a film
16. He just misses catching a bus
17. (a) François Truffaut
    (b) Woody Allen
    (c) Sydney Pollack
    (d) Rob Reiner
    (e) David Cronenberg
18. The Angriest Dog In The World
19. Roger Vadim
20. Rodriguez sold his own blood

SEQUELS

1. Martin Riggs and Roger Murtaugh
2. Terms Of Endearment
3. (a) Exorcist 2 (b) Piranha 2 (c) The Naked Gun 33⅓ (d) House Party 2
4. No guns
5. Palance came back as Curly's twin brother
6. Police Academy
7. The Road Warrior
8. Nigel Kneale

9. The Guns Of Navarone. Force 10 From Navarone
10. Robert Burke
11. Y.M.C.A.
12. Planet Of The Apes
13. Snakes. Bugs. Sheep eyes soup. Chilled monkey brains
14. Concorde
15. A sleazy bar
16. Eric Stoltz
17. Casper
18. Clint Eastwood
19. The Lost World: Jurassic Park
20. Six sequels
    2. Freddy's Revenge
    3. Dream Warriors
    4. The Dream Master
    5. The Dream Child
    6. The Final Nightmare
    7. New Nightmare

THE *EMPIRE* 10

PULP FICTION
1. Jackrabbit Slim's
2) (a) Amanda Plummer (b) Maria de Medeiros (c) Eric Stoltz (d) Peter Greene
    (e) Quentin Tarantino
3. Antwan Rockamora
4. All-American Girl
5. Blueberry
6. Danny DeVito
7. Roger Avary
8. Ezekiel 25:17
9. Palme D'Or
10. Raven McCoy
11. A Douglas Sirk steak
12. Wyatt Earp
13. Big Kahuna
14. 'Girl, You'll Be A Woman Soon'
15. Up his butt
16. 'Shit'

17. Misirlou. Dick Dale And His Del-Tones
18. The waiter Buddy Holly
19. A nurse
20. Because of the metric system

BLADE RUNNER

1. Rachael
2. Phillip K. Dick. Do Androids Dream Of Electric Sheep?
3. Los Angeles, November 20
4. Vangelis
5. The Tyrell Corporation
6. (a) Rutger Hauer (b) Brion James (c) Joanna Cassidy (d) Daryl Hannah
7. David Webb Peoples adapted Blade Runner and wrote the screenplay for The Unforgiven
8. An artificial owl
9. '…but who does?'
10. Snake charmer
11. 1982
12. Retirement
13. Rick
14. Beehive smoke
15. Blade Runner's flying cop cars
16. One, no voiceover; two, unicorn shot; three, ends with the lift doors closing
17. Skin Jobs
18. William Sanderson.
19. An origami unicorn
20. The Shining

TRAINSPOTTING

1. Writer – John Hodge; director – Danny Boyle; producer – Andrew MacDonald
2. Mikey – aka Mother Superior due to the length of his habit
3. Sean Connery
4. Francis
5. Archie Gemmill's goal against Holland in the 1978 World Cup Finals
6. She is still at school
7. (a) Iggy Pop (b) Lou Reed (c) Pulp (d) Underworld
8. Best Adapted Screenplay, Sling Blade by Billy Bob Thornton
9. Jonny Lee Miller

10. Life, a job, a career
11. The Pillow Book, Emma, Brassed Off
12. Carmen
13. 'Shopping!'
14. Alien Resurrection
15. Dale Winton
16. Keith Allen – he plays Hugo in the former, a dealer in the latter. Screenwriter John Hodge also has cameos in both
17. The leisure industry
18. Certificate 18
19. Blondie's Atomic covered by Sleeper
20. 'Just wankers'

GREASE
1. Randall Kleise
2. Danny Zucco
3. Rydell High
4. Sandra Dee
5. Jeff Conaway
6. Jim Jacobs and Warren Casey
7. The T-Birds and The Scorpions
8. Betty
9. Hopelessly Devoted To You
10. Basketball, wrestling, baseball, track
11. Both have animated title sequences
12. Coach Calhoun
13. Xanadu
14. Frankie Avalon
15. Systematic, hydromatic and ultramatic
16. National Bandstand, Vince Fontaine
17. Thunder Road
18. (a) The One That I Want (b) Greased Lightning (c) Summer Nights (d) Grease (e) Sandy
19. Frenchy, Marti, Jan
20. Maxwell Caulfield and Michelle Pfeiffer

ANSWERS

JAWS
1. Quint, Martin Brody, Matt Hooper
2. Amity, Martha's Vineyard, Massachusetts
3. Vertigo
4. John Williams
5. The Sugarland Express
6. Bruce. Robert A. Mattey
7. Lorraine Gary
8. A TV newscaster
9. By screeching his fingernails down a blackboard
10. Great White or *Carcharadon carcharias*
12. USS *Indianapolis*
13. Sterling Hayden
14. Louisiana
15. He crushes a polystyrene cup in one hand
16. *Orca*
17. Universal
18. Show Me The Way To Go Home
19. The Deep
20. He shoots a compressed air tank into the shark's mouth, thus blowing it to smithereens

AIRPLANE!
1. David and Jerry Zucker, Jim Abrahams
2. Leslie Nielsen appears in both
3. Robert Hayes
4. Smoking, drinking, amphetamines, glue-sniffing
5. Steak and fish
6. Charles Dickens
7. Chicago
8. George Zipp
9. Mission: Impossible
10. Ethel Merman
11. The 'Red' zone and the 'White' zone
12. From Here To Eternity
13. 'It's a big building with patients – but that's not important right now'
14. Kareem Abdul-Jabaar
15. Randy
16. Otto

17. 1980
18. There is a beard on the nose of the aircraft
19. A Midsummer Night's Sex Comedy
20. The space shuttle

THE STAR WARS TRILOGY
1. 'A long time ago in a galaxy far, far away...'
2. THX-1138, American Grafitti
3. Episode IV: A New Hope
4. A Wookie
5. Tunisia
6. Grand Moff Tarkin
7. Red 5
8. Industrial Light And Magic
9. Alderaan
10. Obi-Wan Kenobi. The club is called Club Obi-Wan
11. Corvette Summer, The Big Red One, Britannia Hospital, Slipstream, Village Of The Damned
12. Mos Eisley spacesport
13. Spaceballs
14. David Fincher (Alien ^{3}, Seven, The Game)
15. Denis Lawson – he plays Wedge in all three Star Wars films and plays Gordon in Local Hero
16. Frank Oz
17. Clive Revill and Ian McDiarmid
18. '...isn't like dusting crops, boy!'
19. Sir Alec Guinness
20. Blue Harvest was a phoney title used by the Return Of The Jedi production in order to deflect press/fan attention...

THE GODFATHER TRILOGY
1. Fredo, Santino (aka Sonny), Michael, Connie
2. Mario Puzo
3. Winona Ryder
4. Moe Greene
5. '...and I love you, but don't ever take sides with anyone against the family again.'
6. Carmine Coppola and Nino Rota
7. The Cotton Club

8. Adviser or counsel to the Don
9. In a car bomb explosion
10. Connie and Carlo's
11. The Genco Olive Oil Business
12. The Freshman
13. 'I believe In America…'
14. Lee Strasberg
15. Johnny Fontaine
16. The Bells Of St. Mary's
17. a = Vincent Mancini b = Barzini c = Captain McCluskey d = Tom Hagen
    e = Joey Zasa
18. Robert Evans
19. A slice of orange peel
20. Hide out until you get all clear with the other families

THE BLUES BROTHERS

1. John Landis
2. Saturday Night Live
3. A Timex digital watch (broken), an unused prophylactic, one soiled prophylactic, a black suit jacket, trousers, hat and sunglasses. Plus 23 dollars and seven cents
4. The theme from Rawhide and Stand By Your Man. The song that finishes prematurely is Gimme Some Lovin'
5. 1941 and Neighbours
6. Jailhouse Rock
7. 'I've always loved you.'
8. The Good Ole Boys
9. Four fried chickens and a Coke
10. Bazooka, remote control bomb, flame thrower, machine gun
11. Because he jilted her on their wedding day
12. Booker T And The MGs
13. Kathleen Freeman
14. '…We've got a full tank of gas. It's dark and we're wearing sunglasses.' 'Hit it!'
15. $5,000
16. Twiggy
17. When confronted by Carrie Fisher in the sewer
18. a = Aretha Franklin b = Cab Calloway c = James Brown d = Ray Charles
19. It appears on a billboard – it is a line from 2001: A Space Odyssey that director John Landis puts into every one of his films
20. 'And here is your receipt,' is uttered by Steven Spielberg

THE BRAT PACK

1. The Rat Pack
2. Emilio Estevez, Rob Lowe, Andrew McCarthy, Demi Moore, Judd Nelson, Ally Sheedy, Mare Winningham
3. John Hughes
4. (a) Simple Minds (b) John Parr (c) The Psychedelic Furs
5. Duckie
6. S.E. Hinton
7. Sixteen Candles
8. Harry Dean Stanton
9. Demi Moore
10. Her virginity
11. Thieves Like Us by New Order
12. Andie MacDowell
13. Colonel Bogie from The Bridge On The River Kwai
14. A coffin
15. Kelly Le Brock
16. Joel Schumacher. Batman Forever and Batman And Robin
17. James Spader appears in both
18. (a) Rob Lowe (b) Emilio Estevez (c) Andrew McCarthy (d) Judd Nelson (e) Demi Moore
19. She puts the lipstick between her breasts, then buries her head in her cleavage
20. Electric flashes of light that appear in dark skies out of nowhere. St. Elmo's is also the name of a bar the characters frequent

PICTURE ROUND

1. Braveheart. William Wallace
2. Catherine McCormack
3. Patrick McGoohan – he appears in both
4. The Night Of The Hunter. Robert Mitchum
5. A preacher
6. On possession of cannabis
7. Dick Tracy. Al Pacino
8. Breathless Mahoney
9. Vittorio Storaro
10. They were all directed by established actors – Mel Gibson, Charles Laughton and Warren Beatty
11. Anthony Hopkins
12. Robert Redford

13. Arnold Schwarzenegger
14. (a) Robin Williams (b) Tom Hanks (c) Judge Reinhold (d) Dudley Moore
15. Lenny Henry. True Identity
16. Dawn French
17. John Leguizamo. To Wong Foo, Thanks For Everything, Julie Newmar
18. Patrick Swayze, Wesley Snipes
19. Death Becomes Her. Meryl Streep
20. Sweet Bird Of Youth

THE QUIRKY ZONE

OPENING LINES

1. Manhattan
2. The Wizard Of Oz
3. Rebecca
4. Big Wednesday
5. Shallow Grave
6. Love Story
7. Withnail And I
8. Toy Story
9. The Third Man
10. Some Like It Hot
11. JFK
12. Raiders Of The Lost Ark
13. Mean Streets
14. Apocalypse Now
15. Gone With The Wind
16. Taxi Driver
17. Don't Look Now
18. The Maltese Falcon
19. The Apartment
20. Babe

TAGLINES

1. Rocky
2. Arthur
3. The Thing
4. Night Of The Lepus

5. The Addams Family
6. Carry On Henry
7. Heaven's Gate
8. Men In Black
9. The First Wives Club
10. Bonnie and Clyde
11. Sliver
12. Endless Love
13. American Graffiti
14. Basic Instinct
15. Teenage Mutant Ninja Turtles
16. Close Encounters Of The Third Kind
17. Butch Cassidy And The Sundance Kid
18. Gallipoli
19. Shock Treatment
20. Sister Act

CULT MOVIES

1. The Timewarp. The Rocky Horror Picture Show
2. Roderick Jaynes is the pseudonym under which the Coen Brothers edit their movies. Bizarrely, the fictional concoction was nominated for an Oscar at the 1997 ceremony
3. A dog turd, John Waters
4. Peter Jackson
5. Brazil
6. Leslie Ash appears in both – as Steph in the former and as Deborah in the latter
7. (a) The End by The Doors
    (b) Harvey Keitel
    (c) Wagner's The Ride Of The Valkyries
    (d) Hearts Of Darkness
8. Director Stanley Kubrick withdrew it soon after release following incidences of copy cat violence
9. Troma
10. Betty Blue
11. She is buried in the ground up to her neck acting as target practice for the three American debutantes
12. Clerks
13. An ice cream van
14. Slacker

15. William S. Burroughs
16. La Jetée. Chris Marker and Terry Gilliam (Twelve Monkeys)
17. Michael Rooker
18. Russ Meyer
19. A drill – Ferrara is the director of Driller Killer
20. (a) Wild At Heart (b) The Elephant Man (c) Dune (d) Twin Peaks: Fire Walk With Me (e) Blue Velvet

THE NAME GAME

1. Sharon Stone, Basic Instinct
2. Spike Lee, She's Gotta Have It
3. Winona Ryder, Heathers
4. James Stewart, It's A Wonderful Life
5. Rosalind Russell, His Girl Friday
6. Laura Dern, Jurassic Park
7. Nicolas Cage, Raising Arizona
8. Grace Kelly, Rear Window
9. Al Pacino, Heat
10. Kathleen Turner, Body Heat
11. Jeremy Irons, Dead Ringers
12. Woody Allen, Bananas
13. Jane Fonda, Klute
14. Michael Douglas, Wall Street
15. Janet Leigh, Psycho
16. Jon Voight, Midnight Cowboy
17. Jamie Lee Curtis, Halloween
18. Harrison Ford, The Fugitive
19. Cameron Diaz, The Mask
20. Macaulay Culkin, Home Alone

SHITE!

1. (a) Raise The Titanic (b) Electric Dreams (c) Almost An Angel (d) Hudson Hawk (e) Dying Young
2. Tom Wolfe
3. Jessica Lange
4. Patsy Kensit in Absolute Beginners
5. A pair of shoes
6. Warren Beatty and Dustin Hoffman

7. Waterworld
8. Johnny Depp. Plan 9 From Outer Space, Glen Or Glenda, Bride Of The Monster, Jail Bait, Night Of The Ghouls
9. Madonna and Sean Penn
10. Dogs. Diane Keaton and Danny DeVito
11. Helen Slater
12. Amanda De Cadenet appeared in both.
13. A doctor shows his love for the local slut by cutting off her limbs and storing her in a box. Jennifer Lynch is the daughter of David Lynch
14. Annie Lennox
15. Honky Tonk Freeway
16. A New Breed Of Hero
17. The Golden Raspberrys or The Razzies
18. Sgt. Pepper's Lonely Hearts Club Band
19. Irwin Allen
20. Showgirls. Joe Eszterhas

CLOSING LINES

1. GoodFellas
2. The Bridge On The River Kwai
3. King Kong
4. The Usual Suspects
5. The Magnificent Seven
6. Seven
7. Stand By Me
8. On The Waterfront
9. Psycho
10. The Untouchables
11. The Piano
12. Citizen Kane
13. Always
14. Sunset Boulevard
15. Out Of Africa
16. The Big Chill
17. The Sting
18. Local Hero
19. Chariots Of Fire
20. The Color Of Money

ANSWERS

BLOODY HARD

1. Lucille Benson, Susan Blacklinie, Lorraine Gary, Caroline Goodall, Ariana Richards
2. Tootsie
3. Sam Raimi, David Cronenberg, Joe Dante, George Lucas, Steven Spielberg, Frank Oz, Terry Gilliam, Roger Vadim, Lawrence Kasdan, Joel Coen
4. (a) Burt Lancaster in Sweet Smell of Success (b) Kirk Douglas in Ace in The Hole aka The Big Carnival (c) Clifton Webb in Laura
5. Cinematographer Gordon Willis
6. The Apartment in 1960
7. Tim Robbins
8. (a) Martin Scorsese (b) Robert Zemeckis (c) Spike Lee (d) Jane Campion
9. Gere starred in Kurosawa's 1990 film Rhapsody In August
10. The width to height ratio of a printed motion picture frame or the image it projects on a screen
11. Pickpocket
12. She: 33. He: nine. Answer: 42
13. The Native Americans invented popcorn when sprinkling their harvest on hot desert sand
14. Don Siegel, Phillip Kaufman and Abel Ferrara
15. Special effects make up
16. Peter Greenaway
17. 500 Miles by The Proclaimers
18. Bande à Part
19. Westworld, The First Great Train Robbery, Runaway, Physical Evidence
20. Snow White And The Seven Dwarfs
    Pinocchio
    Fantasia
    Dumbo
    Bambi
    Victory Through Air Power
    The Three Caballeros
    Make Mine Music
    Fun And Fancy Free
    Melody Time
    Ichabod and Mr Toad
    Cinderella
    Alice In Wonderland
    Peter Pan
    Lady And The Tramp

Sleeping Beauty
101 Dalmatians
The Sword In The Stone
The Jungle Book
The Aristocats
Robin Hood
The Rescuers
The Fox And The Hound
The Black Cauldron
Basil The Great Mouse Detective
Oliver And Co
The Little Mermaid
The Rescuers Down Under
Beauty And The Beast
Aladdin
The Lion King
Pocahontas
The Hunchback Of Notre Dame
A Goofy Movie
Hercules

TEAM GAMES

SIX DEGREES OF KEVIN BACON

ROBIN WILLIAMS starred in Toys directed by BARRY LEVINSON who also wielded the megaphone on Diner starring KEVIN BACON.

SIR ALEC GUINNESS starred in Star Wars with HARRISON FORD who starred in Raiders Of The Lost Ark, directed by STEVEN SPIELBERG who helmed Hook featuring JULIA ROBERTS who starred in Flatliners with – whatdayaknow? – KEVIN BACON.

MERYL STREEP starred in Death Becomes Her directed by ROBERT ZEMECKIS who made Forrest Gump starring TOM HANKS who shared a space capsule in Apollo 13 with KEVIN BACON.

70s sitcom star JOHN ALDERTON starred in ITV laugh-getter No Honestly with PAULINE COLLINS who appeared in City Of Joy alongside PATRICK SWAYZE who headlined in Ghost alongside DEMI MOORE who played a lawyer in A Few

Good Men, starring KEVIN BACON.

TOMMY LEE JONES starred in JFK which boasts a cameo from KEVIN BACON.

ALPHABET SOUP ASSISTANCE

Q – Dennis and Randy Quaid, Anthony Quayle, Kathleen Quinlan, Aidan Quinn, Anthony Quinn

U – Tracey Ullman, Liv Ullman (Ingmar Bergman star), director Ron Underwood

V – Roger Vadim, Rudolph Valentino, Lee Van Cleef, Jean-Claude Van Damme, Dick Van Dyke, Vangelis, Mario Van Peebles, Robert Vaughn, Paul Verhoeven, Jan-Michael Vincent, Jon Voight

X – Jin Xie (Chinese Film Director), X-rating, Xylophone

Y – Peter Yates, Michael York, Susannah York, Sean Young

Z – Saul Zantz, Darryl F. Zanuck, Richard Zanuck, Robert Zemeckis, Fred Zinneman, David and Jerry Zucker, Ed Zwick

List of Illustrations

ANIMATION
Wallace & Gromit — Aardman Animations
The Lion King — Disney

SCIENCE FICTION
The Day The Earth Stood Still — Moviestore

JAMES BOND
Sean Connery
Pierce Brosnan — Keith Hamshere/UIP

HORROR
Bride of Frankenstein — Universal
Hellraiser — New World Pictures

WESTERNS
Blazing Saddles — Moviestore
John Wayne in The Searchers — LFI

COMEDY
Withnail And I — Murray Close/Feature Film
Gold Rush — BFI

MUSICALS
Singin' In The Rain — MGM
Sound Of Music — 20th Century Fox
Astaire & Rogers in Swingtime — Ronald Grant Archive

CHICK FLICKS
Sleepless In Seattle — Bruce McBroom/Tristar
Casablanca — LFI

BLOCKBUSTERS
Die Hard — Moviestore
Speed — 20th Century Fox

CRIME
Fargo — Michael Tackett/PolyGram
GoodFellas — Warner Bros

THE ACADEMY AWARDS
Oscar — A.M.P.A.S.

HOLLYWOOD COUPLES
Geena Davies & Jeff Goldblum — LFI
Bacall & Bogart — LFI

DIRECTORS
Hitchcock — BFI
Tarantino — Warner Bros

SEQUELS
Alien³ — Bob Penn/20th Century Fox

PULP FICTION — Miramax
BLADE RUNNER — Warner Bros/BFI
TRAINSPOTTING — Liam Longman/Polygram

GREASE
Travolta & car — Kobal
Travolta & Olivia Newton-John — Paramount/BFI

JAWS — Universal/BFI
AIRPLANE — Moviestore
THE STAR WARS TRILOGY — Lucasfilm
THE GODFATHER TRILOGY — Paramount
THE BLUES BROTHERS — Universal/BFI
THE BRAT PACK
Pretty In Pink — Paramount
Breakfast Club — Ronald Grant Archive

PICTURE ROUND
Braveheart — Andrew Cooper/20th Century Fox
Robert Mitchum in Night Of The Hunter — UA/BFI
Dick Tracy — Touchstone
Anthony Hopkins & Mum — Scope Features
Robert Redford — Scope Features
Schwarzenegger — Scope Features
True Identity — Adger Cowans/Touchstone
To Wong Foo… — George Lange/Universal
Meryl Streep in Death Becomes Her — D. Newcomb/Universal

OPENING LINES
Strange Days — Lightstorm

TAGLINES
Jaws 2 poster — Ronald Grant Archive

CULT MOVIES
Pink Flamingos — Entertainment Film
Apocalypse Now — Zoetrope/BFI
Clockwork Orange — Warner Bros/BFI
Wild At Heart — Polygram

NAME GAME
Cameron Diaz in Mask — Entertainment Film
Jane Fonda in Klute — Bob Willoughby/LFI

SHITE!
Four Rooms — C. Barius/Miramax
Boxing Helena — Ruth Leitman/Main Line

CLOSING LINES
Forrest Gump — Paramount

BLOODY HARD
Seventh Seal — BFI
Four Weddings And A Funeral — Stephen Morley/Manifesto
Fantasia — Walt Disney

KEVIN BACON — Kurt Krieger/Famous

ALPHABET SOUP
Alan Alda — LFI
Zemeckis — Sportsphoto